EASY-TO-DO
ENTERTAINMENTS
and DIVERSIONS
with CARDS, STRING, COINS,
PAPER AND MATCHES

(formerly titled: *Winter Nights Entertainments*)

By

R. M. Abraham

DOVER PUBLICATIONS, INC.
NEW YORK

Published in Canada by General Publishing
Company, Ltd., 30 Lesmill Road, Don Mills,
Toronto, Ontario.
Published in the United Kingdom by Constable
and Company, Ltd., 10 Orange Street, London,
W.C. 2.

This new Dover edition, first published in 1961,
is an unabridged republication of the work first
published by Constable and Company Limited in
1932 under the former title: *Winter Nights Entertainments*.

Standard Book Number: 486-20921-0
Library of Congress Catalog Card Number: 61-66705

Manufactured in the United States of America
Dover Publications, Inc.
180 Varick Street
New York, N. Y. 10014

Arithmetick would erre exceedingly,
Forgetting to divide and multiply :
Geometry would lose the Altitude,
The crassie Longitude and Latitude :
And Musick in poore case would be o're-throwne,
But that the Goose Quill pricks the Lessons downe.

TAYLOR, 1630.

PREFACE

NEARLY everyone finds it easy to remember and to repeat, even after a long interval of time, any story which has taken his fancy, but it is quite otherwise when a game or a trick has to be described or shown. This is doubtless because a game must be described exactly, whereas a story can be varied within wide limits so long as its point is remembered and led up to in proper sequence. This book, which was originally a collection of concise notes, to aid a defective memory, is now presented in practically the same form, to children of all ages from ten to three score years and ten, in order to remind them of those simple games and tricks which they will have forgotten.

It is hoped that it will be of some service to invalids who desire to occupy the weary hours of convalescence with pastimes different from those usually indulged in, and that it will enable those unfortunates who have left childhood behind them to return for a moment to that blissful state from which the wise take care never to depart.

R. M. ABRAHAM.

FITZROY SQUARE, W.I.

INTRODUCTION

BY

THE CHIEF SCOUT

The Author, in his Preface, implies that this book is for people between ten and seventy years of age. I rather resent this limitation.

I know a man of seventy-five who has enjoyed learning several new parlour tricks from it in addition to reviving his memory of many old ones—and that's me !

But I recognise also in this book a Treasure Store of games and puzzles for Scouts and Guides, Cubs and Brownies, and, more especially for those of them who are " Handicapts," that is, unable to get about much and largely confined to their rooms or beds. For them these pages will bring many happy hours of interesting occupation.

The Author will thus draw upon himself the blessing both of the youngsters for this fun and of their Scout leaders for the valuable recreative suggestions he has given them.

BADEN POWELL OF GILWELL.

CONTENTS

SECTION ONE

CARD GAMES AND TRICKS

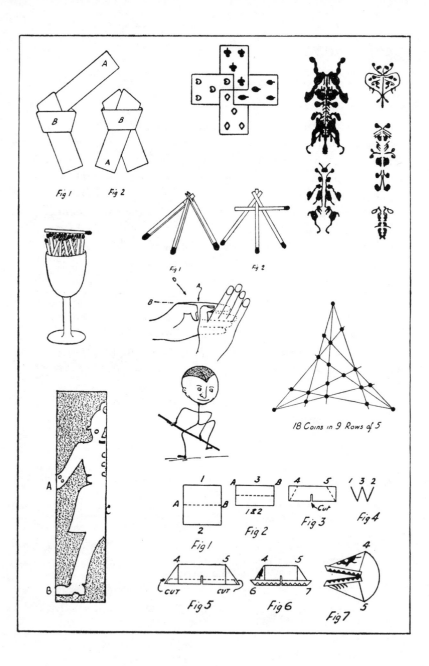

Fig 1

Fig 2

Fig 1

Fig 2

18 Coins in 9 Rows of 5

Fig 1

Fig 2

Fig 3

Fig 4

Fig 5

Fig 6

Fig 7

WINTER NIGHTS ENTERTAINMENTS

I

SPELLING OUT THE CARDS

THIS arrangement of cards is attributed to Lewis Carroll, the author of "Alice in Wonderland." The lay-out of the cards will seem rather tedious the first time it is done, but once the method is grasped the operation does not take very long. The final result comes as a surprise to the onlookers if they have not been told what to expect.

Lay down face upwards the ace, 2, 3, and 4 thus :

1	2	3	4

and below the four cards

2	4	6	8

Then on the lower row place cards with pips equal to the sum of each upper and lower pair of cards in the row thus :

1	2	3	4
3	6	9	Q

Note that Jack counts 11, Queen 12 and King 13. Then continue building up the lower row in the same way, which will at the third move show thus :

1	2	3	4
4	8	12	3

Note that $12 + 4 = 16$ and $16 - 13 = 3$, so place a 3 as shown. When all the cards are exhausted the packs will be thus :

1	2	3	4
K	K	K	K

Then take up all the cards, turning them face downwards as they are lifted, in the following order :

$$K, 4, K, 3, K, 2, K, 1.$$

The King on the right will therefore be at the bottom of the pack and the top card will be an ace.

Then deal the first 13 cards out singly face downwards in 3 rows of 4 cards and one over on the extreme right bottom corner. This is the order in which they should be laid down :

1	2	3	4	
5	6	7	8	
9	10	11	12	13th

Then continue dealing out the next 13 cards, but start by covering the 2nd card, missing out the 3rd, covering the 4th, 6th and so on twice round until the 13th card is placed on the 13th of the first deal. The next lot of 13 cards should start by covering the 3rd card missing out the 4th and 5th, covering the 6th and so on until you arrive at the 13th card. Then the last 13 cards should be started at the 4th card, miss out 3 cards, and cover the 8th and so on. You will now have 13 packs each consisting of 4 cards.

Then take up, still face downwards, the 13th pack, then the 12th, 11th and so on. The last pack taken up will therefore be the top left-hand one. Then spell out O N E, throwing out face downwards a card as each letter is sounded, but turning up the card on the sound of the last letter of each number.

Continue spelling T W O = 2, T H R E E = 3—J A C K, Q U E E N, K I N G—always turning up the card on the sound of the last letter. All the cards will come out in sequence.

2

PICKING OUT ANY NAMED CARD FROM THE PACK

Remove the court cards from the pack and lay down the remaining
40 cards face upwards in this order :

Diamonds	1	2	3	4	5	6	7	8	9	10
Hearts .	10	1	2	3	4	5	6	7	8	9
Spades .	9	10	1	2	3	4	5	6	7	8
Clubs .	8	9	10	1	2	3	4	5	6	7

Then take up the cards face upwards, starting at the bottom left-
hand corner and working upwards thus : 8 of clubs, 9 of spades,
10 of hearts, ace of diamonds, then 9 of clubs, 10 of spades, ace of
hearts, etc. The 10 of diamonds will therefore be the last card taken
up.

Then deal out the cards one by one face downwards in 4 rows of
10 cards. The 8 of clubs will be at the top left corner and the 10 of
diamonds at the right-hand bottom corner. The audience may now
ask for any card in the pack, and the player will be able to turn up the
named card without hesitation. The solution is as follows :

If any diamond is asked for you simply multiply the number by 4
and this will give you its position in the lay-out. For example :

If the 10 of diamonds is asked for then 10 × 4 = 40, and this
card will be number 40, *i.e.,* the card on the right bottom corner. To
find the position of any heart multiply by 4 and add 3. For spades
multiply by 4 and add 6, and for clubs multiply by 4 and add 9. Thus :

Ace of diamonds 1 × 4 = 4th card.

4 of hearts   4 × 4 + 3 = 19th card.

5 of spades   5 × 4 + 6 = 26th card.

9 of clubs   9 × 4 + 9 = 45th card.

The 45th card will really be the 5th card from the top left corner.
After a little practice the calculation may be made very quickly, and
the card turned up almost as soon as it is asked for.

3
TURNING OVER THE CARDS

Set out any ten cards face downwards thus :

☐ ☐ ☐ ☐

☐   ☐

☐ ☐ ☐ ☐

The player is required to start from any turned down card, miss out two cards, turn the 4th card face upwards, and to continue doing this until all the cards but one are face upwards.

The solution of this trick is simple and easily remembered. It is, always to arrange your starting point so that you will turn up the card which was the starting point of the last move. A similar problem worked with coins is given in No. 64.

4
KINGS AND QUEENS

Arrange the Kings and Queens in the following order :

K Q Q K Q Q K K

Then put the top card underneath the pack, turn up the next card and place it on the table. Put the next card underneath, turn up the top card and place it on the table, and so on until all the cards are turned up. They will then be in this order :

K Q K Q K Q K Q

Now ask one of your audience to try to arrange the cards in such order that they will come out as shown above. He will not find the solution very easy unless he lays the cards down on the table in their final order and works the trick backwards. Various such arrange ments may be experimented with in this way.

5
ANOTHER SPELLING TRICK

Arrange the cards in the following order :

Q 4 1 8 K 2 7 5 10 J 3 6 9

the Queen being the top card of the pack. Then spell out O N E— T W O--T H R E E, etc., and as each letter is sounded transfer the top card to the bottom of the pack, but turning up and throwing out on the table the card coinciding with the sound of the last letter of each number. Thus the 1st card O is placed underneath; the 2nd N is also placed underneath; the 3rd E is thrown out and is found to be an ace. Alternatively if you wish to expose the card on the completion of each number then set them out in this order :

3 8 7 1 Q 6 4 2 J K 10 9 5

If the order in which the cards should be placed is forgotten the setting may be found by working the trick backwards.

6
THE SUM OF THE PIPS
(all court cards count 10)

Ask one of the audience to turn up any card in the pack, say a 4, and without showing it to you, to lay it face downwards on the table. Then ask him to build up on the top of this card enough cards to make up with the pips on the first card the number 12, *i.e.*, in this case 8 cards. Then to turn up another card, say it is a 6, and place 6 more cards on the top of it to make 12. Continue doing this until the pack is exhausted except for any cards left over. Then without turning up any card you can calculate the sum of the pips on the bottom cards of the packs. To do this you first count the number of completed packs on the table. Deduct 4 from the number, multiply the result by 13 and add the number of cards left over. This will give the sum required. Thus, suppose there are 9 packs and 4 cards left over. Then 9 less 4 is 5 and 5 multiplied by 13 is 65 and 65 plus 4 is 69, which will be the sum of the pips on the bottom of the 9 packs. If there are no cards left over the sum will be the number of packs less 4 multiplied by 13.

7

A SIMPLER FORM OF THE ABOVE TRICK

Proceed as in trick No. 6 until 6 packs only are on the table. Then the sum of the pips on the bottom of the 6 packs will be equal to the number of cards left over with 26 added. Thus, suppose there are 20 cards left over then the number required will be 20 + 26 = 46.

8

THE CLOCK

Lay out the 13 cards of a suit in the form of a clock, thus.

Ask someone to think of any hour, preferably greater than 6, and another person to give you a number between 15 and 25. You now touch various cards, apparently at random, with your forefinger and ask the person who thought of the hour to add one to this hour each time you touch a card until he reaches the number mentioned by the second person and to tell you to stop when this number is reached.

The last card you touch when he stops you will be the hour he thought of. The method of working the trick is as follows : You mentally deduct 12 from the number mentioned and then touch various cards at random, but let your finger touch the 12 o'clock card when you arrive at the number, then touch 11, 10, 9, 8, 7 and so on, until told to stop, when you will find that you have arrived at the hour thought of.

Example.—Suppose the number mentioned is 20, then 20 — 12 is 8. You touch the first seven cards at random, not forgetting the King so as to confuse the audience, but at the 8th touch place your finger at 12 o'clock, then touch 11 o'clock, 10 o'clock and so on, until told to stop.

9

TREASURE TROVE

Tell this story, elaborating it as much as thought necessary, at the same time laying down the cards as shown, but on the top of one another, in four heaps.

There were four islands	A	A	A	A	four aces.
on which there were diamonds.	D	D	D	D	four small diamonds.
Four gentlemen went to search for them	K	K	K	K	
and took their spades with them.	S	S	S	S	four small spades.
Their wives followed them	Q	Q	Q	Q	
and took their hearts with them.	H	H	H	H	four small hearts.
There are Knaves in every tale	J	J	J	J	
who followed with their clubs, in case, etc.	C	C	C	C	four small clubs.

You will now have four packs with an ace at the bottom of each and a small club face upwards on the top.

Then take up the four packs and deal them out one at a time face downwards, first a row of eight cards then another eight on the top of these and so on until when the 32 cards are out you will have eight packs each containing four cards. Pick up the right-hand pack, then on top of it place the next pack, finally putting the extreme left pack on the top. You will now have four aces at the top of the pack and on laying out the cards you will find that they have come back to the original order. When dealing out the cards into eight heaps, if you do this rather irregularly as in dealing a bridge hand, the fact that they come back to the original order will seem more surprising to your audience.

10

DIVINING THE TOP CARDS

This is a very old and worn trick which, nevertheless, always astonishes the audience if carried out quickly and without hesitation. Get someone to shuffle the cards thoroughly, and while picking up the pack get a sight of the top card. Lay the pack on the table and ask someone to cut it into three heaps. Call out the card which you saw on the top of the full pack and lift up the top card of another heap. Look at it, but do not show it yet. Then call out this card and quickly lift the top card of the next pile. Look at it, call it out and quickly lift the top card of the last heap, which is, of course, the known card and the first one called out. All these cards which you have named are now in your hand and may be shown. It is best to work this trick with not more than four heaps. If you use a greater number the audience will soon discover that the cards are not shown to them as they are picked up, and, moreover, they will find it difficult to memorise more than three or four cards, especially as they do not know beforehand what to expect.

It is fatal to show this trick a second time.

11

TO DETERMINE THE NUMBER OF CARDS MOVED

The effect of this trick is as follows :—

You lay down a row of ten cards face downwards and, turning your back so that you do not see any of the cards, ask a member of the audience to move any number of cards he pleases, *but one at a time* from the left of the row to the right. When he has done this you turn round, and without looking at the face of any card, you immediately turn up a card which has on its face pips equal to the number of cards which he has moved. They can repeat this as many times as they like, moving a different number each time, and you will always be able to turn up a card corresponding with the number they have moved.

The secret of this trick lies in the fact that you can easily calculate the end card each time from the number previously moved. The cards should be laid down in the first place in this order, but face downwards, of course.

1   2   3   4   5   6   7   8   9   10

The cards must be shifted *one at a time* from the left to the right, and this must be done correctly by the players. It is obvious that the first time the cards are shifted the number of cards actually moved will be shown by turning up the extreme right card. It is better, therefore, to shift say two cards yourself and thus show the correct method of moving. The cards will then be in the order

$$3 \quad 4 \quad 5 \quad 6 \quad 7 \quad 8 \quad 9 \quad 10 \quad 1 \quad 2$$

The number of cards now moved by the audience will be shown by turning up the 3rd card from the right. Suppose, for example, they move three cards, the order will then be

$$6 \quad 7 \quad 8 \quad 9 \quad 10 \quad 1 \quad 2 \quad \boxed{3} \quad 4 \quad 5$$

and the 3rd card from the right, which is a 3, will, when turned up, show the number moved by them.

Now suppose that at the second trial they move two cards only, then the order of the cards will be

$$8 \quad 9 \quad 10 \quad 1 \quad \boxed{2} \quad 3 \quad 4 \quad 5 \quad 6 \quad 7$$

You now add 3 to the number moved last time, which was 3 cards, and on turning up the 6th card from the right it is found to be a 2, thus showing them that they moved two cards. You must remember at this stage that five cards have already been moved.

3rd Trial.—Suppose they move one card only, then we have this order :

$$9 \quad 10 \quad \boxed{1} \quad 2 \quad 3 \quad 4 \quad 5 \quad 6 \quad 7 \quad 8$$

and the card which you must turn up is $5 + 3 = $ 8th card, which is an ace.

4th Trial.—Suppose four cards have been moved, then the order is

$$3 \quad \boxed{4} \quad 5 \quad 6 \quad 7 \quad 8 \quad 9 \quad 10 \quad 1 \quad 2$$

and as six cards have been moved already, the card which you must turn up is $6 + 3 = $ 9th card, which is a 4.

5th Trial.—Suppose eight cards moved, then the order is

$$1 \quad 2 \quad 3 \quad 4 \quad 5 \quad 6 \quad 7 \quad \boxed{8} \quad 9 \quad 10$$

and as ten cards have previously been moved, then you turn up $10 + 3 = $ 13th card, which is an 8.

This seems rather complicated at first sight, but a very little practice will enable anyone to work the trick very quickly.

12

ANOTHER METHOD

Trick No. 11 will be a failure if the audience do not move any card at one of the trials.

A variation of the trick which allows for this, is to set out the cards as below, but using the joker as zero and counting it as the eleventh card.

In this trick the cards are to be moved one at a time from the right side to the left. The first order is

10　9　8　7　6　5　4　3　2　1　0

The extreme right-hand card gives the number to use at each trial as a key card, so that if at any time you forget the number previously moved you can turn this card up and look at it. The key card for the first trial is 0, which is counted at the eleventh card. Now suppose three cards have been moved from right to left, and we have this order

2　1　0　10　9　8　7　6　5　4　3

Then on turning up the 11th card from the left it is shown to be a 3 and corresponds with the number moved.

2nd Trial.—Move two cards ; the order is

4　3　2　1　0　10　9　8　7　6　5

and as the key card at the last move was 3 then the 3rd card from the left when turned up is seen to be a 2, the number moved.

3rd Trial.—Move 6 cards, then

10　9　8　7　6　5　4　3　2　1　0

and as key card is 5 the 5th card is the 6, which is the number moved.

It will be seen that it is only necessary to calculate what the extreme right card is and to turn up a card equal to this number from the left end in order to show the number of cards which has been moved.

Now suppose when commencing the 2nd trial the audience refrain from moving a card, then the order will remain

2　1　0　10　9　8　7　6　5　4　3

and as the key card is 3 the 3rd card from the left will be the joker, which equals 0. When you turn it up you will therefore show that no card has been moved.

13

A RUSSIAN PATIENCE GAME

Lay out four cards in a row and throw out the smallest of any two cards of the same suit (ace is high). Fill up the spaces from the cards in your hand and throw out those on the table as long as you can. You will soon arrive at a point where you have four cards of different suits down on the table. You must now cover these with four cards from your hand and again throw out the smallest of a suit. You must endeavour so to move and throw out your cards that you get a vacant space, *i.e.*, to have only three heaps on the table. This vacant space may then be filled up by a card already on the table, thus perhaps uncovering a card which will enable you to start throwing out the smaller cards again.

When you have gone as far as you can and have four cards on the top of different suits you must cover these with four more from your hand. If the spaces are obtained and filled up skilfully it is possible to get all the cards out unless you are blocked by getting aces on the top of the packs. If the game works out you will finally be left with four aces on the table, and all the other cards thrown out. It is, of course, advantageous to get the aces out and down to the bottom of the packs as soon as possible.

14

FOUR FIVES TO COUNT SIXTEEN ONLY

The illustration shows how the four fives can be laid down on the table to show 16 pips only. It will be found that it is not easy to work this out unless you have seen it done before.

15

POKER PATIENCE

In this game for two or more persons each player draws one card from the top of the pack and places it down on the table. The next card as it is drawn must be laid on the table so that it touches a previous card either at the end, the side, or corner to corner. Twenty-five cards are drawn, one at a time by each player, and the final arrangement must be 5 rows of 5 cards. Each player endeavours to so lay down his cards that they will when added up vertically, horizontally and diagonally make the highest possible poker score. The scoring in poker is as follows :

One pair counts   1

Two pairs count   3

A flush counts   5 = 5 cards of same suit.

3 of a kind counts   6

3 of a kind and a pair

          count   10 = full house.

A straight counts   12 = a sequence of 5 cards.

4 of a kind counts   16

5 of a kind counts   20 = 4 of a kind and the joker.

A straight flush counts 30 = a sequence all of the same suit.

A considerable amount of skill is required to play this game successfully, and great care must be exercised in placing the cards to advantage. The other players' cards must be examined as the game progresses, as for example, if you are endeavouring to build up 4 of a kind in one of your rows and the required card turns up in another hand, you will have to try and make that row into a full house or leave it to count 3 of a kind and use the cards to count to advantage in some other direction.

16

THE TOWER OF BRAMAH

This game is generally worked with numbered counters, but it is most conveniently played with the 13 cards of a suit. It is an excellent game to pass the time during the usual after-dinner speech. The method of play is as follows :

Lay down the 13 cards in a pile face upwards, the King underneath and the ace on the top. The game is to transfer all the cards to another pile and in the same order, *i.e.*, King below and ace on the top. Only one card may be transferred at a time, and at no time may a card be underneath one of a higher number. Only 3 piles are allowed during the play, that is, the original pile, the one you are building up, and a transferring pile.

To start play, take off the ace and place it to the right of the original pile. Then take off the 2, place it to the left of the pile and move the ace on to the 2. Then take the 3 from the centre pile and lay it down to the right. Move the ace to the centre, the 2 on to the 3, and then the ace on to the 2.

Then put the 4 down on the left and thus keep on building until all the cards are in a new pile. If you are fond of arithmetic you can work out the number of moves required to transfer any one card to its proper position. Say the 6th card is to be transferred, then the moves which you will have to make will be $(2^6 - 1) - (2^5 - 1) = 32$ and to complete the pile of 13 cards the number of moves will be $2^{13} - 1 = 8,191$. When you have done 13 successfully try 20 ! The origin of this game is supposed to be as follows. At the Creation God placed sixty-four golden discs on one of three diamond needles fixed to a brass plate in the temple at Benares beneath the dome which marks the centre of the world. Day and night the priests transfer the discs according to the laws of Bramah. When all the discs have been transferred the world will vanish into dust. The number of transfers required to complete this task is $2^{64} - 1$ which equals

18,446,744,073,709,551,615.

17

CARD COUNTING

Lay down twelve cards thus :

   1 4 2 8 5 7

   1 4 2 8 5 7

Move the two left-hand cards of the lower row to the right end, thus :

   2 8 5 7 1 4

(leave the top row unchanged for purposes of comparison).

This doubles the first number. Then move the four back again to the left thus :

  4 2 8 5 7 1 which is three times greater than the
            first number.

Then 5 7 1 4 2 8 which is four times greater.

Then 7 1 4 2 8 5 ,, five ,, ,,

and 8 5 7 1 4 2 ,, six ,, ,,

18

Lay down ten cards to count 18 horizontally and vertically.

19

Lay down nine cards to count 17 in three ways.

20

Arrange nine cards so that they count 15 vertically, horizontally and diagonally, *i.e.*, in eight ways.

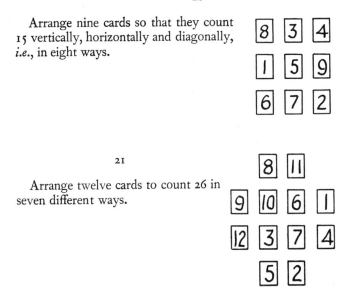

21

Arrange twelve cards to count 26 in seven different ways.

22

COUNTING UP TO FIFTY

Lay out the four sixes, fives, fours, threes, twos and aces, *i.e.*, twenty-four cards altogether. The first player takes up a card, say the four and calls out "FOUR." The next player takes up any card, say the six, and calls out "TEN." The first player then takes up another card, say the five, and calls out "FIFTEEN." Continuing thus the winner is the player who first reaches fifty. At any stage of the game there are certain key numbers which should be aimed for. Another and much simpler form of this game is described in No. 330.

23
THE SIXTEEN COURT CARDS

Without looking at the diagrams below, endeavour to set out the 16 court cards in 4 rows of 4 cards so that each row contains the ace, King, Queen and Knave of different suits both horizontally, vertically and diagonally.

Solution 1 :

A S	K H	Q C	J D
J C	Q D	K S	A H
K D	A C	J H	Q S
Q H	J S	A D	K C

Solution 2 :

A S	K H	Q C	J D
Q D	J C	A H	K S
J H	Q S	K D	A C
K C	A D	J S	Q H

Try to find other solutions.

24
PELMANISM

A good memory for the cards which have been exposed, and the position in which they lie on the table is essential for a successful player of this game. The game can be played by any number of persons. Spread out a pack of patience cards singly and irregularly face downwards on the table. The game is to try to pick up pairs of cards, the player finding the greatest number of pairs being the winner.

Each player plays in turn, the first one starting by turning up any two cards and, if they are not a pair, turning them down again, but not before all the players have seen them. The next player then follows on and should he turn up a pair he retains them and has another try. If his next two cards are not a pair he turns them down and the next player continues.

A good player, when he has turned up his first card can remember the position of another card to make up a pair so that it is possible towards the end of the game to pick up four or five pairs in succession.

The last four cards should not be played.

If there is a large number of players two packs may be used.

25

DEMON PATIENCE

This is probably the simplest and most popular of the many patience games. It is generally played as follows :—

Shuffle the cards well and lay a pile of 7 or 13 cards face upwards on the right. Then lay the next four cards out in a row in front of you and the next card on the left above the first of the four cards thus :

7 or 13 cards.

The game is to build up four packs in the upper row so that each pack is a complete suit. To do this you turn up the cards in your hand three at a time, *i.e.*, exposing every third card, and if a card turns up of the same number as the top left-hand card you may put it up at once into the top row. You can also build downwards on the row of four cards, but only by placing a black card on a red or *vice versá*. When an opportunity occurs you can build up on the top row by transferring cards from the bottom one. When a space occurs in the row of four cards you may fill it up by a card from the pack of 13 cards, and it is in getting spaces and so bringing the 13 cards into play that the difficulty lies. Continue turning over the pack as often as there is any change, three cards at a time, until all the cards have been built up in suits in the top row. Some players put down the four aces in the top row and continue as above until each suit is complete. You may also transfer cards from one pile to another on the bottom row. In this way you can often get a wanted card out from below another which is blocking the game.

SECTION TWO

PAPER FOLDING

A PAPER DRINKING CUP

TAKE a piece of paper about 9 inches square and fold it across the dotted line *A B* in Fig. 1, thus making Fig. 2. Then fold *B* over,

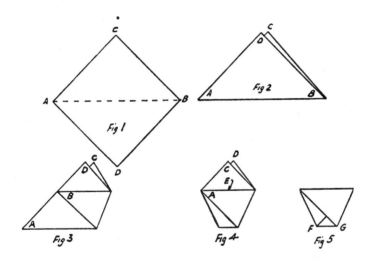

making its top edge horizontal, as in Fig. 3. Turn the paper over and fold *A* as shown in Fig. 4. The two single thicknesses *C* and *D* should now be turned down on opposite sides and tucked into the folds at *E* (Fig. 4), thus making the completed cup shown in Fig. 5. The paper can now be opened out at the top and the two corners *F* and *G* turned outwards so that it will stand on a table.

27

A PAPER AEROPLANE

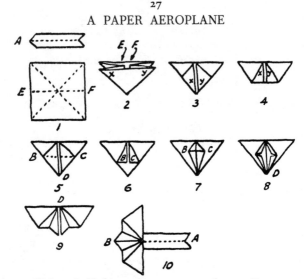

Fig. 1.—Take a half sheet of notepaper and cut off a piece *A* so as to leave a square. Then crease the paper on the dotted diagonal lines. Reverse the paper and crease on *E F*.

Fig. 2.—Bring the sides *E* and *F* together to the centre and press the paper flat.

Fig. 3.—Fold the points *x* and *y* down to the bottom corner of the triangle.

Fig. 4.—Turn the paper over and fold up the points *x* and *y* to the top edge, pressing the crease well in.

Fig. 5.—Open out the last fold which was only made to form a crease on the line *B C*.

Fig. 6.—Turn the corners *B* and *C* down and over to the centre, press the crease well in and open out again.

Fig. 7.—Turn the corners *B* and *C* up and over to the centre, press the crease well in and open out again.

Fig. 8.—Pinch the corners *B* and *C* on the creases just made and press the points which will be formed, in towards the centre.

Fig. 9.—Turn the paper over and fold the corner D up to the top edge and press the crease well in.

Fig. 10.—Open up at the two single thicknesses and insert the piece A. Then crease along the line $A B$, turning up the wings to an angle of about 45 degrees. By bending the tail at A the aeroplane may be made to loop the loop or fly in a circle. You may find that a longer tail than that shown will improve the performance of the model. This will depend largely on the size and thickness of the original sheet of paper used.

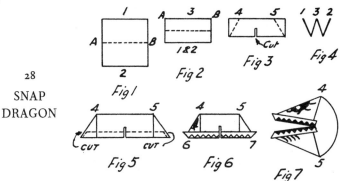

28

SNAP
DRAGON

Fig. 1.—Fold a square sheet across the dotted line $A B$ so that 1 is on the top of 2.

Fig. 2.—Fold 1 up on to 3. Reverse the paper and fold 2 up to 3.

Fig. 3.—Cut the two double thicknesses as shown.

Fig. 4.—The paper when looked at on edge will be as in Fig. 4.

Fig. 5.—Fold on the dotted lines 4 and 5 of Fig. 3 the single thickness backwards and the treble thickness forwards. Then cut through for a depth of about $\frac{1}{2}$ inch where shown in Fig. 5.

Fig. 6.—Fold up the lower edge on the dotted line of Fig. 5. Reverse the paper and make a similar fold. Then ink in the eyes and mouth as shown in Fig. 6.

Fig. 7.—Fold the figure up by bringing points 6 and 7 together. By pressing with first finger and thumb on points 4 and 5 the dragon will snap most realistically.

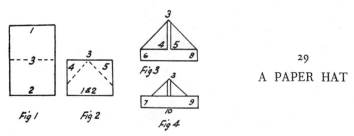

Fig 1. *Fig 2.* *Fig 3.* *Fig 4.*

29

A PAPER HAT

Fig. 1.—Fold the sheet on line 3, bringing 1 down on to 2.

Fig. 2.—Fold corners 4 and 5 over to the centre, making Fig. 3.

Fig. 3.—Fold up the single thickness 6 and 8 covering 4 and 5. Turn the paper over and fold up 7 and 9, thus making Fig. 4.

Fig. 4.—Open out by putting the fingers in at 10 and the hat is complete.

30

CUTTING THE PAPER RINGS

Take three strips of paper about an inch wide and 3 feet long and gum them up into rings as follows :

1st Piece.—Make into a plain ring by joining the face of the paper at one end to the back of the paper at the other end.

2nd Piece.—Give the paper a twist before joining up. The face of the paper at one end will therefore be gummed to the face of the paper at the other end.

3rd Piece.—Join the ends as before, but give the paper two twists.

Then with a pair of scissors cut the rings right round the circumference so as to make two rings $\frac{1}{2}$ inch wide. The resultant rings will be as follows :

1st Paper.—Two rings the same diameter but half the width.

2nd Paper.—One ring double the diameter, but half the width.

3rd Paper.—Two rings as first paper, but they will be interlocked like the two links of a chain.

Various modifications can be made by making further twists and by cutting the rings a second time.

31

A PAPER COCKED HAT

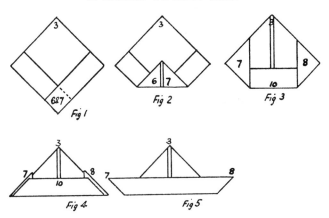

First make a paper hat as shown in No. 29, and by opening out and folding along the vertical line 3—10 in Fig. 4 above, you will make Fig. 1. Then turn up 6 and 7 on the front, reverse the paper and turn up 8 and 9, thus making Fig. 2. Then put the fingers inside the folds and by pulling 6 and 7 and 8 and 9 apart reverse the fold, making Fig. 3. Next turn up edge 10 on to 7 and 8, reverse the paper and turn the back edge up in the same way, which will give you Fig. 4. Then pull out the corners 7 and 8, and the hat as shown in Fig. 5 will be made.

32

A BOX OF CARDS

Bend up 6 visiting cards as shown and fit them up into a cubical box. If the bends are not neatly made and all of the same length the box will not come out square.

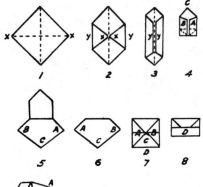

A PAPER TRAY

Fig. 1.—Take a square of strong and not too thick paper. Crease it on the dotted lines and open it out again.

Fig. 2.—Fold the two corners *x x* to the centre.

Fig. 3.—Fold the two edges *y y* to the centre.

Fig. 4. — Turn the paper over and fold across the centre.

Fig. 5.—Put the two forefingers under the parts *A* and *B* in Fig. 4 and open them out. Fold them on the dotted line in Fig. 4, pressing them downwards and flattening them out, thus making Fig. 5.

Fig. 6.—Turn the paper over and do the same fold, making Fig. 6.

Fig. 7.—Fold the corners *A*, *B* and *C* to the centre, turn the paper over and make similar folds on the back.

Fig. 8.—Fold *D* up as shown, turn the paper over and make a similar fold on the back.

Fig. 9.—Pull the flaps *D* and open the creases, when the tray will be formed as shown in Fig. 9.

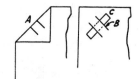

TO BIND PAPERS TOGETHER

Use a pin. If you haven't got one fold down the corner of the sheets and make two cuts as shown at *A*. Open out and push a small folded piece of paper under the slot at *B*.

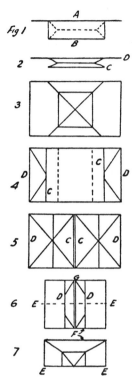

35
A CHINESE JUNK

Fig 8

First make a paper tray as shown in Fig. 9, No. 33, and fold the top edges *A A* down and outwards on to the bottom edges of the box. This is a difficult fold to describe, but easy enough to do when you have grasped the method.

Look at Fig. 1, which is a view of the box seen from the side. The edge *A* should be folded down outwards to touch *B*. To do this you must make an inward crease in the middle of the side as shown by the horizontal dotted line and two triangular creases inwards in each end of the box, also shown dotted. When these creases have been made and the box flattened out it will look from the side like Fig. 2, like Fig. 3 from the top, and when turned over on the back like Fig. 4. Put the box on the table with the opening downwards as in Fig. 4 and turn the two edges *C C* over to the centre on the dotted line. The paper will now be as in Fig. 5. Then turn the edges *D D* over almost to the centre, when you will have Fig. 6. Then fold the lower edge *F* up on to the upper edge *G*, *i.e.*, fold along the dotted line *E E*, thus making Fig. 7. Then grasping the double thickness at *E* and *E* pull them apart and the junk will open out. Then pull up the flaps which will be found inside at each end, when the complete junk will be as shown in Fig. 8.

36

A PAPER PINE TREE

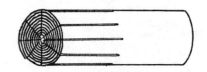

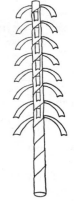

Tear two strips of newspaper about 12 inches wide and as long as possible. Roll them up, not too tightly, placing the beginning of the second piece overlapping about 2 inches inside the end of the first piece. Then cut the end of the roll longitudinally through to the centre in four or five places as shown. These cuts should be made about 6 inches deep, *i.e.*, half way down the roll. Then hold the lower end of the roll in the left hand and pull the centre upwards, when the tree will be formed as shown.

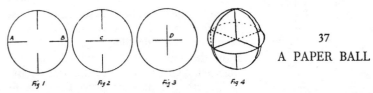

Fig 1   Fig 2   Fig 3   Fig 4

37

A PAPER BALL

Cut out three discs of stiff paper about 3 inches in diameter and with a sharp knife notch them carefully as shown in Figs. 1, 2 and 3. Then bend *A* over towards *B*, being careful not to crease, and pass this portion through the slot *C*. Then bend the two corners of piece 2 and pass them through the double slot *D*.

Straighten out the corners and you will have the skeleton ball shown in Fig. 4. It will be found strong enough to withstand a good deal of knocking about, and there is no fear of its becoming undone.

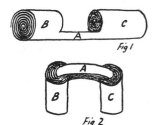

Fig 1

38
A PAPER LADDER

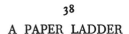

Fig 2

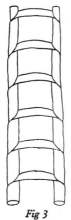

Fig. 1.—Cut a sheet of newspaper in the longest direction about 12 inches wide, and make it up into a roll, but do not roll it up too tightly.

Flatten the roll out in the centre and cut away the portion shown, making the part *A* rather narrow, but see that you do not cut beyond the centre of the roll.

Fig. 2.—Bend the two cylindrical portions back as shown, and, holding them in position with the left hand, pull up the top layer of the narrow central portion, when the ladder will appear as in Fig. 3. You can now stand the ladder up against the pine tree described in No. 36. These two figures are very effective, and children are invariably delighted with them owing possibly to the element of surprise which they contain.

Fig 3

39
A LACE CAP

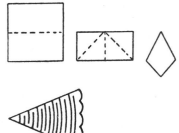

Fold a square of coloured paper as shown and cut the doubled edges a few times. Scallop the lower edge and open out.

40

A PAPER TRAY ON LEGS

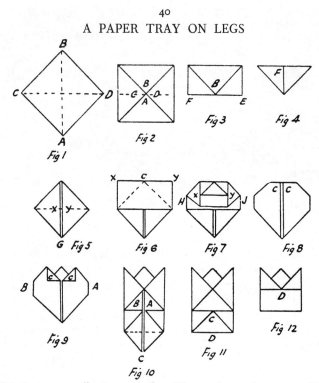

This is a more effective tray than No. 33, but rather more difficult to make the first time it is attempted.

To make

Fig. 1.—Crease a square piece of paper on *A B* and *C D*.

Fig. 2.—Turn the four corners up to the centre.

Fig. 3.—Turn the paper over and fold across the dotted line *C D* in Fig. 2.

Fig. 4.—Fold *F* up to the top edge, turn over and fold *E* up on the opposite side.

Fig. 5.—Put the fingers inside and reverse the opening.

Fig. 6.—Put the fingers underneath the two edges *x* and *y*, open them out, and bring edge *C* up to the top as shown. Turn the paper over and make a similar fold on the back.

Fig. 7.—This is the only difficult fold in this tray. To make it fold the centre of the edge *C* down to the horizontal double thickness as shown and by putting the forefinger inside the corners of *x* and *y*, press these two corners out flat in a triangular form. Then turn the paper over and make a similar fold on the back.

Fig. 8.—Fold edge *H* over on to *J* across the centre line, turn the paper over and make similar folds on the back.

Fig. 9.—Turn the four single corners *C* down so as to make points where they join on to the double thickness.

Fig. 10.—Turn edges *A* and *B* (Fig. 9) over to the centre. Turn the paper over and make a similar fold on the back.

Fig. 11.—Turn the edge *C* up on the dotted line. Make a similar fold on the back.

Fig. 12.—Turn edge *D* up as far as it will go and turn the back edge up also.

Fig. 13.—Pull out flaps *D* and press out the sides, when the tray will suddenly appear.

Fig 13

41

THE HOLE THROUGH THE HAND

Roll a piece of paper into a tube about an inch in diameter and 9 inches long. Hold the tube horizontally in the right hand and look through it with the right eye. Hold the edge of the left hand against the tube, palm towards you, when the object looked at will appear to be seen through a hole in the left hand.

42

A PAPER KETTLE

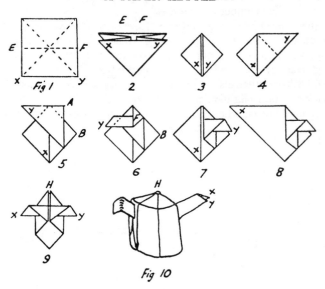

Fig 10

To make.

Fig. 1.—Crease a square of paper diagonally as shown by the dotted lines. Turn the paper over and crease on the horizontal dotted line *E F.*

Fig. 2.—Bring *E* and *F* together and press out flat.

Fig. 3.—Fold *x* and *y* down to the bottom corner. Turn the paper over and make two similar folds on the back.

Fig. 4.—Turn corner *y* back again to its original position.

Fig. 5.—Fold *y* over to the left, making the crease about half-way between the point *B* and the middle line of the paper.

Fig. 6.—The next fold may be found somewhat difficult at first. You must fold *A y* downwards, but as the end *A* is double you can only do this by forming a small triangular fold as shown at *F*. This triangle should at its upper right-hand edge coincide with the edge of the paper underneath.

Fig. 7.—Fold the point *y* to the right and press out flat.

Fig. 8.—Then unbend *x* and make similar folds to those which have just been made on *A y*. Turn the paper over and carry out the same operations on the other side.

Fig. 9.—The paper should now be as shown in this illustration.

Fig. 10.—Bring *x* and *y* together and bring the two similar folds at the back together also. Hold these parts between the thumb and forefingers, pull slightly apart and blow into the small hole which will be found at *H*, when the kettle should open out as illustrated.

43

A CORDON OF POLICE

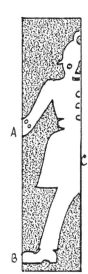

Tear off a strip of newspaper about 6 or 8 inches wide and as long as possible. Then fold over 2 inches at one end, creasing well down, and continue folding, thus making it into a flat roll about 2 inches wide.

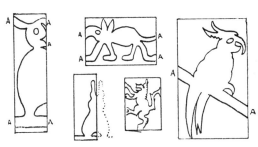

Then cut away the shaded portion, being careful to leave portions *A*, *B*, *C* uncut. When opened out you will have a row of policemen hand in hand.

Many other amusing figures may be cut out, a few being shown on this page.

44

A PAPER BIRD

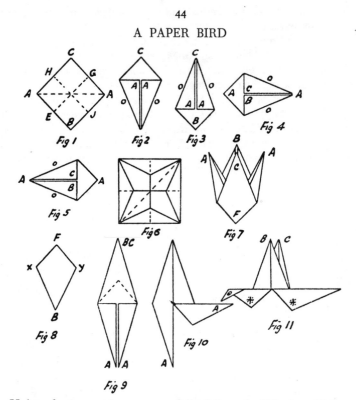

Fig 1   Fig 2   Fig 3   Fig 4

Fig 5   Fig 6   Fig 7

Fig 8   Fig 9   Fig 10   Fig 11

Unless the instructions are carefully followed, difficulty will be experienced in making the paper up into the form shown in Fig. 7. If the creases are carefully made the paper will assume this form naturally.

Fig. 1.—Take a square piece of paper and crease it on the diagonal *A A*, pressing it well down. Turn the paper over and crease it on line *E G*, pressing the centre portion well down, but leaving about an inch at each edge not so heavily creased. Do the same on line *H J*.

Fig. 2.—Turn the two edges *B A* over on to the line *C B* and crease the edges well down from *B* to *O* only.

Fig. 3.—Undo the last folds made and turn the two edges *C A* over in the same way, but downwards, creasing down the portions *C O* only. Undo these folds.

Fig. 4.—Turn the edges *C* and *B* over on to the line *A A* and crease down from *A* to *O* only.

Fig. 5.—Make similar folds, but from the opposite direction.

Fig. 6.—The paper when opened out should be like Fig. 6. The dotted lines show the creases on one side of the paper and the full lines those on the other side. The end portions at *E G H* and *J* should now be creased in the opposite direction, *i.e.*, they should be on the same side as the diagonal *A A*.

Fig. 7.—If these creases have been made carefully the four points *A A B* and *C* may be brought together by pinching the points *A A* so that the diagonal crease is inside.

Fig. 8.—Bring the four points together and press the paper flat.

Fig. 9.—Fold points *B* and *C* on the line *x y* and on opposite sides and upwards, thus enclosing the triangular part *F*.

Fig. 10.—Bend point *A* over to the right to form the tail of the bird and the other point *A* to the left to make the beak. Hold the two points * (Fig. 11) between the thumbs and forefingers and by pulling them apart the wings will flap.

45

A PAPER VASE

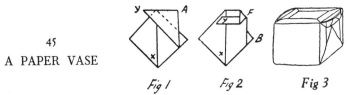

Fig 1   *Fig 2*   *Fig 3*

To make this vase proceed as in No. 42 until you have made Fig. 4. Then when making Fig. 5 do not bend the point *y* so far over to the left, but make it as shown in Fig. 1 above. Then when bending *A y* down make this fold narrower and the triangle in consequence smaller. Continue all the other operations as in No. 42. The result of these shorter bends is to make a large opening in place of the small hole *H* in the kettle. The parts *x* and *y* at each side can be curled round and tucked in to make the handles shown in Fig. 3.

46

A PAPER CRUET

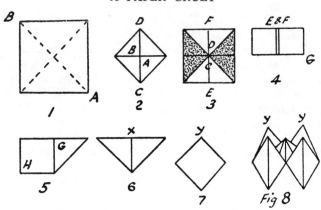

Fig. 1.—Crease a square piece of stout paper on the dotted lines.

Fig. 2.—Fold the four corners to the centre.

Fig. 3.—Turn the paper over and again fold the four corners to the centre. Colour the two triangles shown shaded or paste a small ornament from a Christmas cracker on to these parts.

Fig. 4.—Fold across the centre, bringing E up to F and with the coloured parts inside.

Fig. 5.—Turn the corner G up level with the top edge.

Fig. 6.—Turn the paper over and fold H up level with the top edge.

Fig. 7.—Put the two forefingers into the opening at x and by separating them reverse the fold, thus forming a square.

Fig. 8.—There are now four single thickness corners at y. When these are opened out the cruet should be as illustrated.

If you now put your fingers and thumbs down into the four sections of the cruet and turn it bottom outwards you can, by separating the fingers and thumbs of each hand, show the coloured part, or by separating the hands and closing the fingers and thumbs cause the coloured part to disappear.

47

A FANCY TEA CLOTH

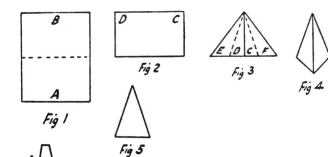

Fig 1

Fig 2

Fig 3

Fig 4

Fig 5

Fig 6

Take a piece of newspaper and fold it on the dotted line as in Fig. 1, thus making Fig. 2.

Fold C and D down, making Fig. 3. Then fold E and F down once or twice, making Fig. 4. Then fold the paper over on the centre line, making Fig. 5. Then cut portions of the edges away as shown in Fig. 6 or in any way you fancy, and the paper when opened out will be as shown or, of course, more elaborate if you have made more cuts in the edges. Note that portions A, B, C, D, E, F in Fig. 6 must be left intact when cutting out the gaps in the folded edges. If the bottom portion is not cut the cloth will come out as a square with a fancy pattern in the centre.

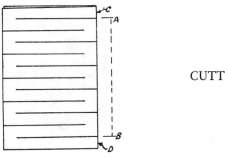

48
CUTTING A HOLE

In a piece of paper 6 inches square, to cut a hole of such a size that it is possible to pass it over your body. To do this fold the paper along the middle line and make several cuts from each side as shown. Then cut the doubled edge from *A* to *B*, leaving the parts *C* and *D* uncut. You can now open the paper out into a large ring.

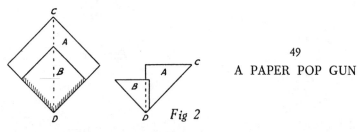

Fig 2

49
A PAPER POP GUN

Take a piece of thin cardboard about 6 inches square and a piece of strong thin brown paper *B* about 4 inches square. Lay *B* on *A*, turn over the lower edges of *B* and gum them to the back of *A* along the shaded portion only. When dry fold both pieces on the dotted line *C D* with the paper *B* inside. Then hold the cardboard between the thumb and forefinger by the point *C*. Give a sharp swing forward and downwards when the paper *B* will fly out, as shown in Fig. 2, with a sharp report.

50

A MODEL AEROPLANE

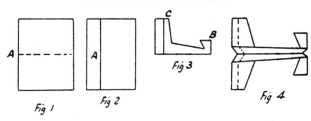

Take a sheet of writing paper and open it out as in Fig. 1. Fold the edge *A* over about half an inch two or three times. Then fold the paper on its original crease and cut the double thickness on the line from *C* to *B*. Crease back the wings and tail as shown, when the aeroplane will be complete as in Fig. 4. By a judicious trimming of the wings and by bending the tail it can be made to loop the loop very gracefully.

51

PAPER CHAIN DECORATION

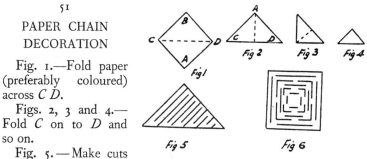

Fig. 1.—Fold paper (preferably coloured) across *C D*.

Figs. 2, 3 and 4.— Fold *C* on to *D* and so on.

Fig. 5.—Make cuts in the doubled edges as shown.

Fig. 6.—When opened out the paper will be perforated as in this figure. Make a number of these and gum the square portion in the centre to a similar square in the next paper. Make as many as necessary and then join the four corners to the similar corners of the next lot, when a very decorative chain will be formed.

52

CAT BOX OR WATER BOMB

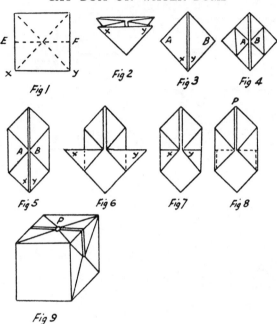

Fig 1   Fig 2   Fig 3   Fig 4

Fig 5   Fig 6   Fig 7   Fig 8

Fig 9

Fig. 1.—Crease a piece of paper diagonally as shown by the dotted lines. Turn the paper over and crease on the horizontal dotted line EF.

Fig. 2.—Bring E and F together and press out flat.

Fig. 3.—Fold x and y down to the bottom corner, turn the paper over and make two similar folds on the back.

Fig. 4.—Fold the corners A and B to the centre.

Fig. 5.—Make two similar folds on the back.

Fig. 6.—Fold the corners x and y outwards on the front and then on the back.

Fig. 7.—Fold the points of x and y inwards to the centre on the front and back.

Fig. 8.—Open out the folds *A* and *B* in Fig. 4 and tuck the four triangular pieces *x* and *y* into the folds.

Fig. 9.—Blow into the small hole which will be found at *P*, and the box will open out. The completed box may be filled with water and will explode with a loud report if thrown against a wall or dropped from a height on to the pavement.

53

FOLDING A *BILLET-DOUX*

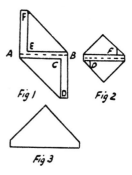

Here is one of the ways our grandmothers folded their love-letters before the invention of the modern envelope.

Fold the bottom left-hand corner *C* over nearly to the centre line *A B* as in Fig. 1. Then fold corners *D E* and *F* in this order, making Fig. 2. Then fold on the line *A B* so as to bring the four corners already folded inside.

Then tuck flap D under flap F, thus interlocking these corners and completing the folding as in Fig. 3.

54

HERE IS ANOTHER METHOD

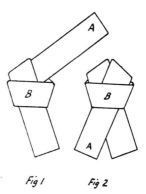

Fold the note over lengthwise, making it into a flat band about an inch wide. Then tie a knot by folding over the end as shown in Fig. 1.

Finally pass end *A* under *B* as shown in Fig. 2.

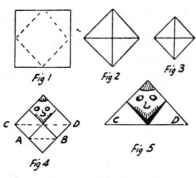

Fig 1   Fig 2   Fig 3

Fig 4   Fig 5

55
THE LAUGHING MAN

Take a square of paper and fold the four corners over to the centre, making Fig. 2. Turn the paper over and again fold the four corners to the centre. On the other side paint a man's face on the single thickness flap and crease along the nose so that a ridge will stand outwards. Turn the paper over and fold across the dotted line *A B*. Turn the paper front side up and fold along the dotted line *C D*, tucking the point underneath the face of the man. The inside of the mouth may be coloured if desired. By pulling and pushing *C* and *D* the mouth opens and shuts.

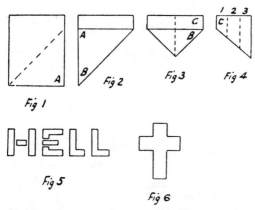

Fig 1   Fig 2   Fig 3   Fig 4

Fig 5   Fig 6

56
HELL

Take a piece of paper as Fig. 1 and fold the corner *A* up as shown in Fig. 2. Fold corner *B* up as in Fig. 3, and then fold on the dotted line, making Fig. 4. Make two cuts with a pair of scissors as shown by the dotted lines. On arranging parts 2 and 3 they make up Fig. 5, while part 1 when opened out will be as Fig. 6. You can hand the pieces out to your friends and make up any story you consider appropriate.

57

A DOUBLE BOAT

Fig. 1.—Take a square of paper and fold it on the dotted line *A B*.

Fig. 2.—Fold it on the dotted line *C D*, thus making a square.

Fig. 3.—Fold on the dotted lines and over to the centre *G*, thus making Fig. 4.

Fig. 4. — Turn the paper over with the plain side uppermost and fold down the two front layers at *H*, pushing the corners out sideways into triangular creases as shown, making Fig. 5.

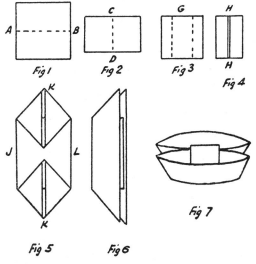

Fig. 5.—Fold the edge *J* over to *L* on the line *K, K* making Fig. 6.

Fig. 6.—Open out, thus making the completed boat (Fig. 7).

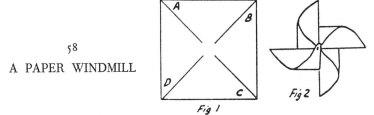

58

A PAPER WINDMILL

Take a square sheet of paper, and with a pair of scissors cut nearly to the centre from each corner. Prick a hole in the centre and at points *A, B, C* and *D* with a pin. Turn these four corners over to the centre, but do not crease, and pass a pin through them, through the centre hole and into the end of a cane.

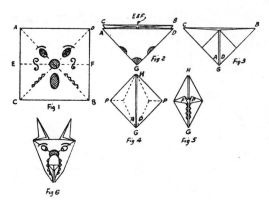

THE WILD MAN FROM BORNEO

Fig. 1.—Take a square sheet of paper and fold it on the dotted line *E F*. Undo this crease, turn the paper over and fold on the line *C D*. Undo this crease and fold on the line *A B*. Turn the paper over and paint the nose, eyes, teeth and mouth as shown in Fig. 1.

Fig. 2.—If the paper has been well creased it will be easy to bring the points *E* and *F* together. Press out flat, thus making Fig. 2.

Fig. 3.—Fold the points *A* and *D* down to *G*.

Fig. 4.—Turn the paper over and fold the points *C* and *B* down to *G*.

Fig. 5.—Turn the right half of the edge *H P* over to the centre line *H G* and press down the crease from *H* half way only. Open out and fold the edge *P G* to the centre *H G*, press down the crease half way and open out again. You should then have two creases as shown by the dotted diagonal lines. Make similar creases on the left side. Turn the paper over and do the same on that side. If these creases have been properly made and pressed down, the next operation will be simple. Lay the paper down flat on the table. Take the two front points *P P* between the thumb and first finger of each hand, pinch the sides together, making a horizontal crease and press them inwards towards the centre line *H G*, bending the paper on the diagonal creases just made. Do the same on the back side, when the paper should be as shown in Fig. 5.

Fig. 6.—Hold the paper between the thumb and first finger of the left hand by the two points *P P* on the side where the teeth have been painted, and blow into the hole which will be found at *H*. The head of the man will gradually appear and then the horns will shoot upwards if a little assistance is given with the right hand. When the figure is fully formed, open the mouth and pull out the two triangular folds to make the tongue. Colour the tongue red.

60

A ROYAL AIR
FORCE CAP

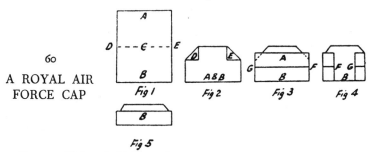

Fig. 1.—Take a half sheet of newspaper and fold it at *C* by bringing *A* down to *B*.

Fig. 2.—Turn down the double corners *D* and *E*.

Fig. 3.—Turn up the front half *A* twice.

Fig. 4.—Turn the edges *G* and *F* over backwards.

Fig. 5.—Turn up the single part *B* twice.

61

A PAPER BAND

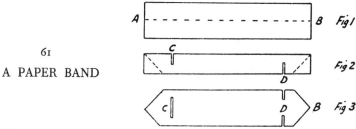

Fig. 1.—Fold on the line *A B*.

Fig. 2.—Cut off the corners on the dotted lines. Cut half-way through the double thickness at *C* and cut half-way through the two single parts at *D*.

Fig. 3.—Open out and pass *B* through the slot *C* until the notches *D* engage in this slot.

62
BOOMERANG

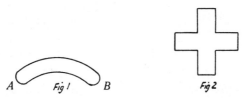

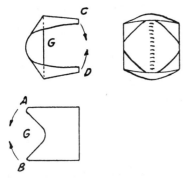

Cut out a segment of a circle about 2 inches long from a thin postcard. Stick the edge *A* underneath the thumbnail of the left hand, holding it there horizontally. Then flick the edge *B* with the forefinger of the right hand, which will send the card spinning away from you. It will return to the thrower as well as an ordinary boomerang.

Another form which is equally good is shown in Fig. 2.

63
A PAIR OF SUGAR TONGS

Fold a visiting card as shown. If the corners *A* and *B* are pressed inwards the parts *C* and *D* will be brought together and may be used as a pair of sugar tongs. The easiest way to fold the card is to take the two long edges between the thumb and second finger of the left hand. Then press these edges outwards, *i.e.*, towards the left, push the centre of the card *G* inwards, *i.e.*, to the right, with the first finger of the left hand and at the same time bring the two short edges together with the finger and thumb of the right hand.

COIN TRICKS AND GAMES

64

THE FIVE-POINTED STAR

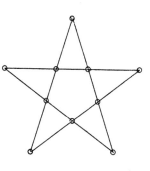

Draw a five-pointed star on a sheet of paper as shown in the illustration. The game is to put your finger on an empty crossing, pass over the next crossing, and lay a coin down on the next one. Continue doing this until all the cross-lines except one have been filled up. The solution is simple and easy to remember. All you have to do is to start each time from a point which will allow you to fill up the point from which you started the previous move.

65

HOUDIN'S COIN COUNTING

Spread about 25 coins on a tray and cover them with a cloth. Bring them into the room and momentarily uncover the coins. Then ask the company to guess how many coins are on the tray. Then vary the number or lay them out in the form of a cross, square or star and let the company try again.

It is said that Houdin trained himself to count up to fifty objects at a glance.

66

THE DIAMETER OF A PENNY

How many pennies placed in a pile will it take to equal in height the diameter of a penny? If you try this you will be surprised to find that it requires 19 or 20.*

*If you are using an American penny, the answer will be 12 or 13.

67

BRUSHING A COIN

Place a shilling* in the palm of your hand and hold the hand out in front of you, palm upwards. Ask someone to try with an ordinary clothes brush to brush the coin down to the tips of your fingers, using a straight brushing movement only. It will be found impossible to move the coin away from the centre of your palm.

68

COIN AND HANDKERCHIEF TRICK

Put a coin in the middle of a handkerchief, pass the four corners through a ring and pull taut as shown in the illustration. You are required to remove the coin while all four corners of the handkerchief are held. To do this pull one edge A up through the ring, when the coin can be released and the ring removed.

If the handkerchief is covered with another during this operation the company will be very mystified.

69

THE EIGHT COINS TRICK

Set out four silver and four copper coins alternately (or black and white draughtsmen or four cards face up and four face down).

The game is to move any two adjacent coins and in four such moves to bring all like coins together.

Here is the solution :

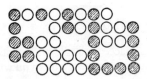

*Use any coin at all for this trick.

70

ARRANGE TEN COINS TO FORM FIVE ROWS
OF FOUR COINS

(for solution see No. 64)

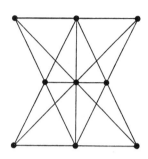

71

ARRANGE NINE COINS TO FORM
TEN ROWS OF THREE COINS

72

ARRANGE SIXTEEN COINS TO
FORM FIFTEEN ROWS OF
FOUR COINS

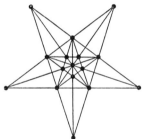

73

ARRANGE NINETEEN COINS TO
FORM NINE ROWS OF FIVE
COINS

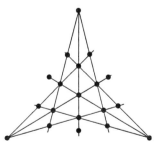

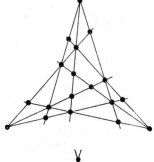

74

ARRANGE EIGHTEEN COINS TO FORM NINE ROWS OF FIVE COINS

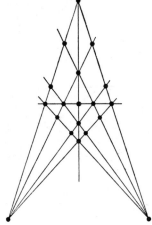

75

ARRANGE NINETEEN COINS TO FORM TEN ROWS OF FIVE COINS

76

CARD AND PENNY

Hold the left forefinger upright and lay a visiting card on its tip. On the top of the card balance a penny. Then with the thumb and forefinger of the right hand flick the edge of the card sharply. The card will be forced away and the penny will be left balanced on the tip of the forefinger.

77
COUNT ELEVEN WITH THREE COINS

Place three coins on the table. Pick them up one at a time counting "one, two, three." Then lay them down on the table one at a time, counting "four, five, six." Pick up one counting "seven," then another counting "eight." Slide the last coin along the table counting "nine," but do not pick it up, then lay down the two coins in your hand counting "ten, eleven." Then pick up the three coins, hand them to someone, and ask him to count "eleven." He will probably start by putting the three coins down on the table as he counts "one, two, three," and will therefore not be able to make eleven unless he slides the sixth coin instead of picking it up, as you did with the ninth.

78
Q TRICK

Set out any number of coins or counters in the form of a Q. Then ask someone to count any number he chooses, starting at the tail of the Q and working round to the left. Then to count the same number backwards, *i.e.*, from left to right, but to continue round the circle and miss out the tail. You can then tell him the counter at which he stopped. This trick seems to mystify the average person, although it is obvious that the counter at which he stops will be the same distance from

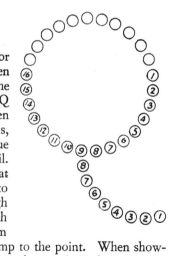

the stump of the tail as from the stump to the point. When showing this trick it is necessary to change the number of counters in the tail at each trial, or the audience will notice that they always stop at the same counter no matter what number they choose.

79

THREE HEADS AND THREE TAILS

Lay down six coins, three heads up, and three tails up, with one space between the two groups. The game is to change the coins end from end moving only one coin at a time. A coin may jump over one adjacent coin into an empty space, or it may be moved one space into an empty space. Heads up may only move to the right and tails up only to the left. The diagram shows a solution. Try to find others.

80

SIXPENCE AND TUMBLER

Lay down two pennies on the tablecloth and a sixpence between them but not touching.* Then place a tumbler over the coins so that its edges rest on the two pennies. The problem is to get the sixpence out from below the tumbler without touching either. To do this scratch the table cloth with the nail of your forefinger. The coin will gradually work its way out under the edge of the tumbler.

81

CAMEL THROUGH THE EYE OF A NEEDLE

Cut a hole in the centre of a piece of paper the exact size of a half-penny.† If you bend the paper slightly a half crown may be passed edgewise through the hole.

---

*Or substitute nickels for the pennies, and a dime for the sixpence.
†Or cut a hole the size of a quarter and pass a half dollar through it.

TRICKS WITH MATCHES

82

TEN MATCHES IN PAIRS

SET out ten matches thus :

```
  1  2  3  4  5  6  7  8  9  10
  |  |  |  |  |  |  |  |  |  |    10 Matches thus
  ||  |  |     |     |  |  ||  |    1st 4 to 1 8 6 to 9
  ||  |  ||     |     |     ||  |    Key Move 8 to 3
  ||     ||     ||     ||     ||     3rd 2 to 5 & 10 to 7
```

The problem is to lift a match, cross over two matches and lay it down next to the third one, thus making one pair. Continue doing this until you have made five pairs. A solution is shown above.

Another solution is to move 5 to 2, 7 to 10, 3 to 8, 1 to 4, and 9 to 6. *A variation* may be made in this trick if the double matches are counted as one. The solution will then be 5 to 2 and 7 to 10—3 to 8 and 1 to 6, then 9 to 4.

82A

Another variation is to use eight matches only. The solution will then be 5 to 2—3 to 7—4 to 1, and 6 to 8.

A solution may be found for *any even number* of matches greater than eight as follows : Move 4 on to 1, thus making a pair at the left hand. Then move 6 on to 2. Continue doing this until eight matches are left. Then the eight matches can be paired as shown above.

82B

Another variation is to take 12 matches and make them into four piles each containing three matches by moving over three matches each time. Here is a solution : 7 to 3—5 to 10—9 to 3—12 to 8—4 to 10—11 to 8—2 to 6, and 1 to 6.

Now try to make 16 matches into four piles of four matches.

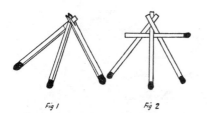

Fig 1   Fig 2

83

LIFTING THE TRIPOD

Make a slit in the end of a match and sharpen the end of another one to a chisel point. Push the chisel end into the slit and prop up the two matches thus fastened together, by means of another match resting lightly against the point, as shown in Fig. 1. The trick is to lift these three matches by a fourth one. To do this gently insert the fourth match horizontally as shown in Fig. 2 and tilt the two fixed matches backwards until the top of the loose match falls on to the one held in the hand. Then lower the horizontal match until the two fixed ones fall down over the loose one, when all three may be lifted as shown.

84

WITH SIX MATCHES TO FORM FOUR
EQUILATERAL TRIANGLES

To do this, form a triangle on the table and then hold the other three matches up over them, thus forming a pyramid, as shown in the illustration.

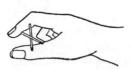

85

A TRICK FOR THOSE WITH SUPPLE
FINGERS

Try to hold two matches as shown in the illustration.

86

THE MOORISH STOOL

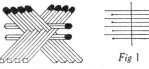

Fig 1

To lay down nine matches on the table and lift them all at the same time with one more match. To do this lay the matches down as in Fig. 1. Then lay the 10th match on the top of the others parallel with the lowest match. By lifting the two central matches together all may be lifted at once. It is more attractive to lift only the first match laid down, when the eight matches will fall in the form of a Moorish stool, the weight of this top match keeping the others in position.

87

THREE MATCH BRIDGE

Three matches arranged as shown and supported on the edges of three books or wineglasses will support a pile of coins on the centre triangle. Four matches can also be arranged in a similar manner.

88

ARRANGE FIVE MATCHES TO COUNT FOURTEEN

This is the solution :

II

I

I

I

———

14

———

89

NINE

Lay down six matches as below.
The problem is to add five more and make nine only.
Solution :

```
| | | | |
N I N E
```

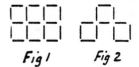

Fig 1   Fig 2

90

SIX SQUARES INTO THREE

Lay down 17 matches to make 6 squares. The problem is to remove
5 matches and leave 3 of the original squares. This may be done as
in Fig. 2.

91

COLLECTING THE MATCHES

This is an excellent and very amusing game for several persons.

Each player is given two matches and is allocated a different number,
say 1 to 5 if there are five players. The players lay their matches
down on the table. The banker, who must be good at " telling the
tale," endeavours to collect all the matches in this fashion. If he calls
out " one " and knocks on the table before No. 1 does so he takes one
of his matches. If any player knocks on the table in mistake he loses
a match. The banker tells some story and tries to work in the words
" one " to " five " when the players are amused and laughing at the
downfall of one of their number. He also tries to work up a heated
argument about the fairness of one of his captures, and can generally
score a point or two in this way. It is remarkable how quickly a good
spieler can collect all the matches, in spite of every precaution taken
by the players not to be caught unawares.

92

THUMBS AND FINGERS

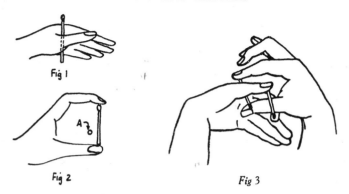

Fig 1

Fig 2

Fig 3

Put a match into the hollow between the thumb and forefinger of each hand as in Fig. 1. The trick is to transfer them both at the same time to the opposite hands and on the points of the fingers as in Fig. 2. Fig. 3 shows how this is done.

93

A VARIATION OF NO. 92

Hold a match as in Fig. 2, No. 92 in the left hand and another one in the right hand, this match being in the position shown at *A* (Fig. 2), *i.e.*, the two matches are interlocked, that in the left hand being vertical, the right one horizontal. The trick is to separate the hands so that both matches are clear of each other. The secret is to get the head of the match well wedged into the first joint of the finger of the left hand. Pull smartly with the right hand, sliding its match along the left thumb to the point at the same time slightly separating the thumb and forefinger of the left hand, thus making a gap through which the right hand match may pass.

It is desirable to have a little practice before showing the trick.

94

THE DISAPPEARING NAME

Take a booklet match between the finger and thumb, the match being at right angles to the finger. Show the name printed down the side of the match.* Roll the match over and at the same time turn the hand over and pretend to show that the name is printed on the other side. Then turn the hand over without rolling the match and show that the name has disappeared. Roll it over and turn the hand again, thus showing that it has disappeared from the other side also. It can then be made to appear again on both sides. This is a variation of the old die trick described in No. 309.

Fig 1   Fig 2

95

NINE SQUARES INTO TWO

Lay down 24 matches to make 9 squares, as shown in Fig. 1. The problem is to remove 8 matches and leave two squares only. The solution is shown in Fig. 2.

96

SPILLIKINS

Put a boxful of wooden matches into an egg cup or liqueur glass as shown in the illustration. The first player takes a match out of the cup and lays it across the top of the remainder. The next player does likewise. This is continued until all the matches are horizontal, or have fallen on the table. The player who disturbs one of the matches balanced across the top of the others so that it falls on the table wins that match and loses a mark. The player with the least number of matches is, of course, the winner.

---

*Since many matches have no name imprinted on them, it may be necessary to mark one side.

97

ONE SIXTH INTO UNITY

This trick is very difficult except perhaps to mathematicians. Lay five matches down thus :

$$\frac{I}{VI}$$

Fig. 1

which is supposed to represent the fraction $\frac{1}{6}$.

The problem is to make the fraction into unity by the addition of 1 match. The solution is

$$\frac{I}{V\,I}$$

Fig. 2

This represents 1 divided by the square root of 1, which, of course, equals 1.

98

FIFTEEN MATCH GAME

This is a short game for two persons.

Lay 15 matches on the table. Each player takes alternately either 1, 2 or 3 matches at a time, as he chooses. The loser is the one who is left with the last match. To win it is only necessary to leave, first, 13 matches, then 9 and then 5 for your opponent to pick from. A more complicated game of the same nature is described in No. 22.

99

THE TWENTY-ONE MATCH GAME

This game is similar to No. 98, but is played with 21 matches. To win it is only necessary to take up enough matches to make four taken at each turn, or in other words to always leave an uneven number for your opponent to pick from If the first player takes three matches then the second takes one. Then if the first takes 2 the second takes 2 also, so that the first player must be left with the last match.

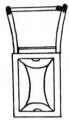

100

WHICH MATCH?

Open a match-box slightly and fix two matches in the sides, heads upwards. Spring another match in between them as shown in the illustration. Then set the horizontal match alight at the middle of its length. Which of the two side matches will be ignited first? Try it and see.

101

THE LOVERS' KISS

Take two booklet matches and fix one with its head upright by closing the tray of a wooden match-box on it. Lean another match against the upright one head to head. Then light the inclined match in the middle. The inclined match will stand steadier if the lower end is split and the two parts spread apart. There are several variations of this trick in circulation.

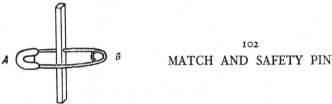

102

MATCH AND SAFETY PIN

Remove the head from a large wooden match and push a safety pin through the middle of it as shown in the illustration. Hold the pin horizontally between the thumb and second finger of the right hand at *A* and between the thumb and forefinger of the left hand at *B*. With the forefinger of the right hand press the top half of the match back towards you and let it go quickly. The match will spring back and appear to cut through the safety pin.

103
THREE AND A HALF DOZEN

Hand six matches to a mathematician and ask him to lay them down on the table so that they will make three and a half dozen. This is how it is done :

I I I V I

104
NINE TO MAKE TEN

Lay down four matches and by adding five more make ten :

I I I I
TEN

105
TAKE SEVEN MATCHES, REMOVE ONE AND LEAVE NOTHING

I I I I I I NIL

106
TO MAKE TWO TRIANGLES WITH FIVE MATCHES

107
TO MAKE EIGHT SQUARES WITH FIFTEEN MATCHES

108
TO MAKE FIVE TRIANGLES WITH NINE MATCHES

109

FORM THREE SQUARES AND TWO TRIANGLES WITH NINE MATCHES

To do this, set four matches on the table in the form of a square. Set two matches up at each end for the two triangles and the 9th match to form the apex of the triangle. You will then have a triangular prism fulfilling the conditions. To actually form the figure the assistance of a little plasticine will be required.

See No. 84 for a similar trick.

110

BALANCING THE MATCH BOXES

The illustration shows the old gentleman who balances a number of empty match-boxes for the edification of theatre queues.

This trick is done by pushing the tray of the first box down about a quarter of an inch, and as each box is balanced on the top of the next one below, its tray is pushed down into the vacant space in the cover of the previous one.

SECTION FIVE

STRING TRICKS AND FIGURES

INTRODUCTION

PLAYING with a piece of string has always had a great fascination for man ever since prehistoric times. The weaving of string figures is probably one of the earliest pastimes of primitive people, and the most general in its distribution over the inhabited globe. Owing to the fact that the present generation of natives of Africa and the Pacific Islands are more interested in acquiring the vices of the white man than in practising their own ancient games, the art of making string figures has been in danger of being lost. Thanks, however, to the interest taken in recent years by anthropologists and others, about 500 different figures have now been collected and described, and their significance has been studied in relation to the habits and environment of the various tribes. Some of the figures are very complicated and difficult to construct successfully, and, when completed, are not in themselves very interesting or effective ; while others are most attractive, easily made, and quite suggestive of the objects or actions they are supposed to represent. Men of science have divided the figures into three classes.

In class A the figures are supposed to represent some object, or to produce a decorative design. Class B are usually made as an accompaniment to a story. Class C are more in the nature of conjuring tricks and are intended to create a surprise effect.

Those who see string figures made for the first time are nearly always interested and amused ; and, if they can be induced to construct a few themselves, generally find the pastime most fascinating. With a little practice, constant at first, they can acquire a pastime which may fill in the time while waiting for the kettle to boil.

The best string for the production of most of the figures is one made of silk about one-tenth of an inch in diameter and about 7 feet long. This should be knotted into a closed loop or preferably spliced (the best knot to use is described in No. 174), as a knot sometimes interferes with the free sliding of the strings over each other. The majority

71

of figures are started in one way; and it is a curious fact that the same method of starting is used by natives in every part of the world.

This would seem to indicate that there has been more intercourse between primitive races than has been generally supposed, or possibly that as the games are so old their distribution may be due to the fact that they were in common use before the land was split up into the continents as we know them at present. The starting moves referred to are called for convenience *Opening A*. The first part of this opening is called the *first position* and is shown in Fig. 1. It will be seen that the loop is placed between the thumb and first finger of the left hand, carried across the palm, between the 3rd and 4th fingers, round the back of the 4th finger, across to the back of the 4th finger of the

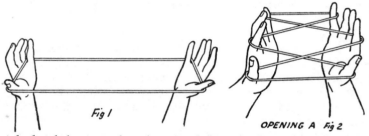

Fig 1

OPENING A Fig 2

right hand, between the 4th and 3rd fingers, across the right palm, between the 1st finger and thumb, round the thumb and then over to the back of the thumb of the left hand. To complete opening A the 1st finger of the right hand is placed from below, under the string crossing the palm of the left hand, and picks up the string on the back of the finger. The hands are then separated, thus drawing the left palmar string to the right and making all the string taut.

The left index finger is then put down through the loop which has just been made by the right index finger, and picks up from below the right palmar string on the back of the finger. The hands are again separated, thus making Fig. 2, which shows opening A completed. Note in the descriptions which follow that the near string means the string nearest your body.

Navahoing the Loop.—This is a very usual movement. It is performed by taking hold of the lower loop on any digit, lifting it up over the upper loop or loops on the same digit and dropping it on the palmar side of the hand.

During the weaving of the figures the hands are usually held upright, palms facing each other; and generally speaking the strings should be kept taut by extending the hands as far apart as possible. It is important to place the strings symmetrically on the fingers, and to keep the loops clear of each other where they encircle the fingers, as otherwise, when the figure is completed, it will be distorted or fall into knots. When breaking up some of the figures it is desirable to release the loops from the fingers in a certain order, as if this is not done the string will be drawn into a knotty tangle.

During the construction of a figure, should a mistake be made, or a string accidentally dropped, it is well to start again from the beginning. If, however, you do continue with the figure, you may discover a new construction which you will probably not be able to reproduce unless you are gifted with an exceptionally good memory. The simplest figure, and one of the most universal is the three-pronged spear, which is made as follows :—

III

THREE-PRONGED SPEAR

1st.—Place the string on the hands in position 1.

2nd.—Pick up the left palmar string from below with the back of the right index, at the same time rotating this finger anti-clockwise one complete turn, *i.e.*, through 360 degrees.

This will put two twists on the palmar string.

3rd.—Extend, pulling the strings taut.

4th.—Put the left index down through the loop just made as near the right index as possible and pick up from below with the back of the left index the right palmar string. Extend, drawing the strings taut.

5th.—Drop the strings off the right thumb and right fourth finger and draw the hands apart, thus forming the spear shown in the illustration.

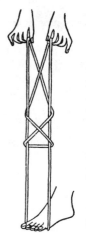

112

THE TREE CLIMBER

Use a long string for this figure.

This is a most effective figure. It is supposed to represent a tall cocoanut tree up which a native climbs step by step, getting smaller as he nears the top.

1st.—Hold the left hand palm upwards, fingers pointing away from you, and lay the single string of the loop across the four fingers, letting the long loop hang down.

2nd.—Pass the forefinger of the right hand towards you, into the long loop and with its back and without twisting the strings, lift up the loop over the finger-tips of the left hand, passing one string between the first and second fingers and the other string between the third and fourth fingers of the left hand. Draw taut, bringing the hands up into the normal position. See No. 121.

3rd.—Bring the right forefinger over towards the left palm, pass it from above round the far side of the little finger string, up into the long loop and over the near string. Then pass it down into the loop on the left forefinger, and with its front pick up the palmar string of this small loop.

4th.—Draw this string out to the right. This will allow the loops which are on the back of the right forefinger to drop off on to the horizontal strings.

5th.—Draw the loop on the front of the right forefinger out a little farther, place the toe into this loop and hold it down on the ground.

6th.—Transfer the left forefinger loop to the right forefinger and the left little finger loop to the left forefinger.

7th.—Raise the right and left forefinger alternately, when the little man will climb up the tree in a most realistic manner.

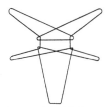

113

THE FLYING BIRD

1st.—Opening A.

2nd.—Put the foot on the far little finger string and hold the string down on the ground.

3rd.—Pick up from below, on the backs of the fourth fingers, the two far index strings.

4th.—Navaho the little finger loops.

5th.—Pick up from below on the backs of the thumbs the two near index strings.

6th.—Navaho the thumb loops.

7th.—Release the index fingers.

By rotating the wrists the bird will flap its wings.

114

AN ESKIMO HOUSE

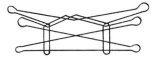

1st.—Opening A.

2nd.—Put the four fingers of each hand down into the thumb loop and throw the near thumb string over both hands.

3rd.—Bend the thumbs away from you over one string and under all the others, and pick up from below on the backs of the thumbs the far little finger string which comes from the wrists.

Return the thumbs, bringing the far strings back with them to the front.

4th.—Pull the two strings crossing the backs of the hands over the fingers, drop them on the palmar side and extend. This forms the house.

Release the forefingers and extend, when the house is supposed to collapse and two little boys to run out of a door at each end.

The vivid imagination of an Eskimo is required to appreciate this effect.

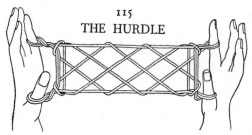

115
THE HURDLE

A long string is necessary for this figure.

This is a very effective figure which always creates surprise owing to the fact that the final design appears so suddenly from what seems to be a tangle of strings. It is very easily made, but the strings must be placed symmetrically on the fingers.

1st.—Position one.

2nd.—Pick up the left palmar string from below by the back of the right hand.

3rd.—Pick up the right palmar string from below by the back of the left hand.

4th.—Bend the thumbs away from you over one string, and with their backs pick up from below the near little finger strings and return.

5th.—Bend the little fingers towards you and with their backs pick up from below the far thumb strings. You should now have two loops on each little finger, two on the thumbs and a string round each wrist.

6th.—With the left hand grasp the bunch of strings where they cross in the centre. Pass the right thumb from the near side under all these strings and with the left hand pull them over towards you, letting them rest in the hollow between the right thumb and first finger. Then with the left thumb and first finger lift the two loops which encircle the right thumb up over the point of the thumb, and let the bunch of strings fall back over the point of the right thumb. Then replace the two loops on the thumb in their original position. Do the same movement with the left thumb. Draw the hands apart and see that all the strings are properly placed.

7th.—Lift the two strings from the backs of the wrists and let them fall on the palmar side. Extend the hands, when the completed figure will suddenly flash out as shown in the figure. Variations in the figure may be made by picking up the strings in a different order.

To break up the figure release the thumb loops.

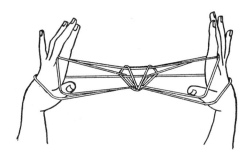

116

**THE FRUIT
BLOSSOM**

Use a long string.

This figure, which consists of a hexagonal pyramid or a tent held up by guy ropes, is a very striking design and easy to make.

1st.—Opening A.

2nd.—Insert the four fingers of each hand from above into the thumb loop and throw the near thumb string over the backs of the hands.

3rd.—Put the thumbs up into the wrist loops.

4th.—Twist the right thumb over towards you, then down under the two wrist strings and up from below into the little finger loop. Turn the thumb with its back down and pick up the far little finger string, bringing this string under all the others and back to the normal position.

5th.—Put the left thumb from the near side and from below up into the right thumb loop close to the thumb, and separate the hands.

6th.—Move the loops from the first fingers on to the little fingers.

7th.—Pick up the far thumb strings on the backs of the fourth fingers.

8th.—Pick up from below the two near little finger strings on the backs of the index fingers and release the loops on the thumbs.

9th.—Pick up from below with the back of each thumb the upper near index finger string. Then release the loops from the little fingers and draw the hands apart.

117

THE PARACHUTE

1st.—Place the string on the right hand only in position one.

2nd.—Hold the right hand horizontal, palm towards you, letting the long loop hang down. With the left thumb and finger draw the palmar string in between the thumb and first finger of the right hand, down the back of the hand and up through the long loop, across the palm and hang the loop on the right index finger.

3rd.—Draw out on the palmar side the string which passes between the 3rd and 4th fingers and hang the loop on the right thumb.

4th.—With the left finger and thumb lift the string which crosses the back of the fingers over to the palmar side and draw it out to the left, at the same time see-sawing the right hand to enable the strings to slide over each other. Turn the right hand above the left as shown in the illustration, when the parachute will be formed.

118

SLIPPING THE LASSO

Hold the string up in the left hand, letting it fall in a loop in front of you. Put the right hand into the loop from the far side. Turn the hand downwards and anti-clockwise away from you round the right string and then towards you until the hand is horizontal, fingers pointing to the left, thus picking up the right string on the back of the hand.

Pass the hand behind the left side of the loop, bring it up anti-clockwise, then between the two strings of the loop and back to the horizontal behind the left string of the loop. Then separate the hands in a vertical direction, when the double loop will be released from the wrist.

119

CRUSHING THE
COCOANUT

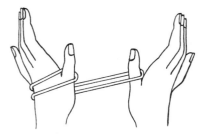

1st.—Place the loop over both thumbs. Then twist the four fingers of the left hand clockwise under the two strings, thus giving the position shown in the illustration.

2nd.—Turn the left hand palm downwards, fingers pointing to the right, and bring the right hand above the left and closer to your body.

3rd.—Pick up the two strings which pass across the back of the left hand on the back of the little finger of the right hand. Pull the right hand towards you and draw the strings taut with the hands in the normal position.

4th.—Put the little finger of the left hand down between the thumb and fingers of right hand and pick up from inside and below on the back of this finger the two strings running from the right thumb. Draw taut.

5th.—With the right hand lift the strings on the back of the left hand over the fingers and thumb, drop them on the palmar side and draw taut.

6th.—Drop the string from the little fingers and clap the hands together to crush the cocoanut. Draw the hands apart, and the cocoanut will disappear.

120

TYING THE KNOT

The problem is to grip the two ends of a string and to tie a knot in the middle of it without letting the ends go. To do this lay the string down on the table in front of you. Then fold your arms and grip the left end of the string with your right hand and the right end with your left hand. Draw the hands apart, and a knot will be formed in the centre, thus satisfying the conditions laid down.

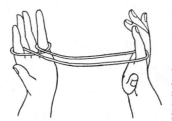

121

THE DISAPPEARING LOOPS

1st.—Hold the left hand, palm upwards, fingers pointing away from you, and lay the single string of the loop across the palm, one string hanging down between the thumb and first finger, the other string outside the little finger.

2nd.—With the right hand lift up the long loop which is hanging down, and draw it upwards over the tips of the left fingers, so that one string passes between the first and second finger and the other string between the third and fourth fingers of the left hand. Draw taut.

3rd.—With the right hand grasp the two strings of the long loop close to the palm of the left hand, and pass the two parts of the string which run from the right hand into the hollow between the left thumb and first finger and then round the thumb, the string coming from the little finger being below.

4th.—Pass the strings away from you over the tips of the fingers of the left hand, placing the upper thumb string between the first and second fingers and the lower one between the third and fourth fingers.

5th.—Draw the strings forward over the finger tips, placing one between the first finger and thumb and the other outside the little finger.

6th.—Remove the two loops from the left thumb and pull the long loop to the right, when all the strings will come away from the hand.

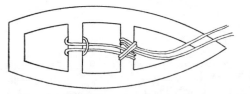

122

CASTING THE
DINGHY ADRIFT

Here is a dinghy, the towing rope being fastened to the yacht. The problem is to cast the dinghy adrift without unhitching the ends of the rope from the yacht.

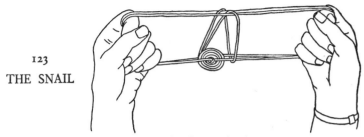

123

THE SNAIL

1st.—Lay the string down in the form of a figure 8.

2nd.—Put the two forefingers down into the far loop and the two thumbs down into the near loop. Separate the hands and bring them up into the normal position. Each string will now have a crossing on it.

3rd.—With the left hand hold the two right index strings near the right forefinger and rotate the right forefinger so as to twist the two strings four or five times. Do the same with the left index finger.

4th.—Put the thumbs from below up into the corresponding index loops and navaho the thumb loops.

5th.—Bring the two index fingers together and the two thumbs together and slide the loops on the right hand on to the corresponding finger and thumb of the left hand. The right hand is now free of the strings.

6th.—Holding the left hand horizontally, thumb towards you, pass the 2nd, 3rd and 4th fingers of the right hand towards you under the two strings hanging down the near side of the left thumb and grip them close to the thumb.

7th.—With the right thumb and forefinger, grip the two strings on the near side of the left index finger and remove the left hand from the strings.

8th.—Pass the four fingers of the left hand from the far side towards you into the loop of two strings which has just been removed from the left index finger.

9th.—Draw the hands apart, when with a little shaking and manipulation the body of the snail will roll up as shown in the illustration. The figure can be made to crawl back and forth by inching the fingers of the right hand.

THE GALLOPER

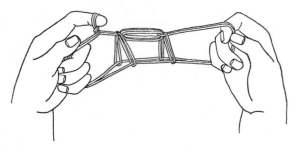

This is a most effective but somewhat complicated figure to construct. When it has been made a few times it is comparatively easy, although the construction naturally takes longer than most of the other figures.

1st.—Make the lightning flash described in No. 125.

2nd.—Pick up from the back with the back of both thumbs the double strings which run diagonally from the index fingers to the bottom string, and remove from each index finger the three loops on it.

3rd.—Put each index finger from below into its thumb loop, and on its back pick up its far thumb string, thus releasing each thumb from one of its loops. The thumbs will now, if they are turned away from you, be in the little finger loops.

4th.—With the back of each thumb pick up the far little finger string, and, by turning the thumbs down and towards you, bring this string to the front and the hands into the normal position.

5th.—Put the right thumb and forefinger down through the left index loop, lift the left thumb loop off the thumb, bring it up through the index loop and replace it without change on the thumb. Do the same to the left little finger loop, and make a similar movement on the right hand.

6th.—Lift up each index loop and put it over the whole hand down on to the wrist.

7th.—Hold the far thumb and near little finger strings of the left hand by the first finger and thumb of the right hand, and remove the left hand from all the strings. Transfer the two strings held by the right thumb and forefinger to the left hand, holding them between the second and third fingers of that hand.

8th.—Hold the far thumb and near little finger strings of the right hand by the first finger and thumb of the left hand and remove the right hand from all the strings.

All the strings are now being held in the left hand. Keep the loops separated so that they do not get mixed up, or you will have some difficulty in the next move.

9th.—Put the right fourth finger away from you into the original right thumb loop and the right thumb away from you into the original left thumb loop. Then take hold of the other two loops by the right thumb and forefinger, thus releasing them from the left hand.

10th.—Put the left fourth finger away from you into the original right finger loop and the left thumb towards you into the original left finger loop and extend the hands.

The horse will now be spreadeagled out with eight strings forming the body and four loops for the legs.

11th.—Bring the near thumb and far finger strings together at the bottom of the figure and the far thumb and near finger strings to the top, thus bringing the body and legs of the horse upright.

12th.—Pass the hands as shown in the illustration into the double loops at each end and extend. Then pass the left forefinger away from you over the double string at the top, pick up this string and by revolving the finger towards you bring this top string between the palm and the palmar string. Continue revolving the left forefinger clockwise until it is upright, which will throw a hitch on the string and form the head of the horse.

By manipulating the wrists, the legs of the horse can be made to move and buck jump in a very amusing manner.

To break up this figure, spreadeagle the hind legs and pull them apart.

When making the 11th move it is convenient to lay the strings down on the knees, but after a little practice this is not necessary.

125

A LIGHTNING FLASH

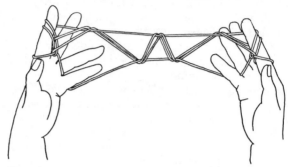

1st.—Put the index fingers only into the loop, but make the far index string very short, keeping the index fingers upright. Throw a small upright crossed loop on the far index string and put the two index fingers from the near side into this loop. Draw the hands apart. You should now have two straight near index strings and two crossed far index strings. Keep the upper index strings on the tips of the fingers and the lower strings at the base of the fingers.

2nd.—Bend each thumb away from you over the near lower index string, and with its back pick up from below the lower far index string and return.

3rd.—Bend each thumb away from you over the upper near index string, and with its back pick up from below the upper far index string and return.

4th.—Bend each little finger towards you over the upper near index string and with its back pick up from below the lower near index string.

5th.—Bend each index finger away from you down into the triangle near the little finger, and with a twist pick up from below on the back of the fingers the upper near index string.

6th.—Turn the palms away from you and release the thumb strings, when the figure will flash out suddenly.

This figure may be continued, to make the galloper described in No. 124.

126

CHURCH STRUCK BY LIGHTNING

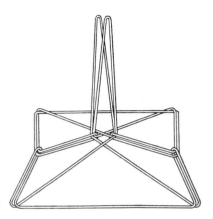

Use a long string for this figure.

1st.—Take up the string in the first position.

2nd. — Bend each index finger down and away from you over the far string and with its back pick up this string and return. You will now have a string on each hand running diagonally from the back of the little fingers to the near side of the index finger round this finger and over to the back of the opposite index finger.

3rd.—Pick up this diagonal string with the back of each thumb by passing the thumb between the string and the palm. Bring it under the thumb string, thus allowing this string to slip over the thumbs on to the palm.

4th.—Bend each little finger towards you over one string and pick up the next string, from below. Then turn each thumb inwards and away from you and pick up the nearest string, from below.

5th.—Place the right index finger down between the two parallel strings and pick up from below the left straight palmar string. With the left index pick up from below the right palmar string.

6th.—Navaho the index loops on both hands.

7th.—Lift up the two index loops off these fingers and hold them in the teeth. Extend the figure, making the strings held in the teeth rather long, thus forming the spire of the church.

8th.—Release the strings in the teeth and separate the hands, when the string will fall to the ground, thus representing the destruction of the church by lightning.

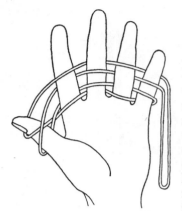

127

THE FIVE BOY SCOUTS

Hold the left hand horizontal, palm downwards, fingers pointing to the right. Hang the loop on the little finger and turn the hand upright. Hold the loop by the right thumb and forefinger close to the little finger and give it a twist counter - clockwise through 180 degrees, placing the twist in the hollow between the third and fourth fingers. Then place the third finger into the long loop from below. Make a clockwise turn through 180 degrees and place the second finger into the long loop. Draw the string tight between each twist. Then make a counter-clockwise turn and place the forefinger into the long loop. Then (and this is important) make a clockwise turn through 360 *degrees*, and place the thumb into the long loop. Make a counter-clockwise turn of 180 degrees on the outside of the thumb, and, passing the long loop over the point of the thumb, draw it away from you, thus tightening the string against the back of the thumb. Then another counter-clockwise turn through 180 degrees and put the forefinger into the long loop. Then a clockwise 180-degree turn on the middle finger, a counter-clockwise 180-degree turn on the third and finally a clockwise turn on the little finger. Release the two loops from the thumb and draw the long loop away from you, when all the turns will pass through the fingers and the string will be released. When putting the loops on the thumb it is desirable to keep it well separated from the forefinger.

Then by bringing the thumb and forefinger together, the loops on the thumb will slip off easily. This explanation seems long and elaborate, but the trick only takes two or three seconds to complete after a little practice. Note that the twists must be made in the following order, starting from the little finger : Counter 180 degrees, clock 180 degrees, counter 180 degrees, clock 360 degrees, counter

180 degrees, counter 180 degrees, clock 180 degrees, counter 180 degrees, clock 180 degrees.

This is the nearly true story which should be told when showing the above trick. It can be amplified as much as is thought desirable:

Once upon a time five Boy Scouts were captured by savages, and to prevent their escape they were tied up with a long rope, so . . . starting first at this little one and winding the rope round the waists of all the others in this way, and then back again. They were then fastened up to a post in the middle of the dancing saloon. When it got dark this little fellow (the thumb), with the thirty-three stars on his shirt sleeve, wriggled his way up to the surface and released all the others so. . . . When the savages came to look for them the next morning, they had all gone home and left the empty rope lying on the ground with this end still tied to the post.

128

SCISSORS AND STRING

The trick is to remove the loop from the scissors while the ends are being held by someone else.

To do this. Pass loop *A* down through *B*, draw it out and then pass it from above down over the points of the scissors, draw it over the thumb pieces, when it will be released. If the loop *A* is above the two strings, then pass this loop over the points from below upwards. In either case the loop *A* must be passed through the ring *B* on the same side as the strings pass through *B*.

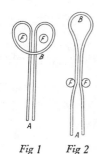

Fig 1   Fig 2

129

REVERSING THE LOOP

Make a loop *B* as shown in Fig. 1 and pass the first and second fingers, represented by *F F*, through from the side on which *B* lies, *i.e.*, away from you. The trick is to bring the part *B* through to the other side and up as shown in Fig. 2 without releasing the two ends *A*.

To accomplish this hold the loop *B* by the thumb of the left hand. Pass the index and second fingers of the right hand through and away from you as shown at *F F* (Fig. 1). Then spread these fingers wide apart, bend them downwards and towards you, at the same time throwing the back of the right hand away from you and pulling the string taut. Then close the two fingers, thus gripping the loop which has been formed on *B*. Reverse the motion of the right hand, keeping the fingers closed, let go the thumb of the left hand, thus bringing the loop *B* up into the position shown in Fig. 2. The secret lies in spreading the fingers apart. When anyone is asked to try the trick he invariably keeps the fingers together and cannot therefore succeed.

130

CUTTING THROUGH THE BUTTONHOLE

Pass the loop of string through your buttonhole and hold it taut by passing a thumb through each end. Bring the thumbs close together and away from you so as to still hold the string taut. With the palm of the right hand uppermost, pick up the lower string coming from the left thumb by the inside of the little finger of the right hand. Then pick up the lower string on the right thumb by the inside of the little finger of the left hand, taking care that this string is below all the others. Draw the strings taut. Put the left thumb down into the left little finger loop, dropping it off the little finger, thus releasing the loop originally on the thumb. Simultaneously drop the loop off the little finger of the right hand, and separate the thumbs, when the string will appear to have cut through the buttonhole.

131

THE STICK AND CHAIR

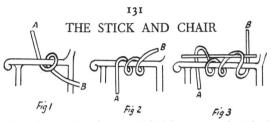

Fig 1   Fig 2   Fig 3

(1) Stand in front of a chair and, holding a scarf with the end *A* in the left hand, with the right hand wind the end *B* round the arm as shown in Fig. 1.

(2) Transfer the end *B* to the left hand, pull it across the arm to the left and with the right hand pull the end *A* across to the right, thus making Fig. 2.

(3) Then lay a walking stick on the top of the scarf, and, holding *A* in the left hand, draw it to the left above the stick and then downwards. At the same time hold *B* in the right hand, draw it to the right above the stick down under the arm of the chair, and up again on the other side, thus making Fig. 3.

Pull *A* up to the right round the arm and knot *A* and *B* together with a reef knot. Then pull the stick out, and the scarf, although seemingly tied securely round the arm of the chair, will come away with the knot still intact.

132

THE BRACELET

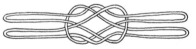

The strings must be kept loose during the weaving of this figure, and a short string should be used.

1st.—Opening A.

2nd.—With the mouth draw the far little finger string towards you above all the strings, and release the little fingers.

3rd.—With each little finger cross above the two index strings and pick up from below the far thumb string. Release thumbs.

4th.—With the back of the index fingers pick up from below, the mouth loop close to the mouth. Release mouth.

5th.—Navaho the index finger loops.

133
THE FLY ON THE NOSE

Hold the string between the thumbs and fingers about 8 inches apart, and let the long loop hang down in front of you. Bring the right hand towards you and to the left, carrying the string to the left, thus forming a small pendant loop on the top part of the long loop. Hold the crossing of the loop between the fingers and thumbs and then grip this crossing between the teeth, allowing the small pendant loop to hang down over the chin. With the left hand hold the large loop by both strings horizontally in front of you and level with the mouth. Put the first finger of the right hand towards you into the small loop from the far side. Turn this finger in a half-circle anti-clockwise, *i.e.*, downwards, then towards the right, up, and then towards the left until the finger is opposite the nose.

This will put a twist on the small loop. Close the fist except the first finger, and place this finger from below between the two strings of the long loop, which all the time is being held out horizontally by the left hand. Place the finger on the point of the nose. Release the string from the teeth and pull the left hand, when the string will come free from the finger.

134
MAKING A WOOLLEN BALL

Make a ring of cardboard about $2\frac{1}{2}$ inches in diameter, the hole in the centre being about 1 inch. Wind this ring with odd lengths of differently coloured worsted, as shown in the illustration. When quite full cut the worsted strands with a pair of scissors right round the circumference of the ring clear through to the centre hole, but be careful not to cut beyond the centre.

Then pass a piece of strong string round the cut and tie the ends tightly with a reef knot. The cardboard ring can then be torn away and the ball trimmed up where necessary with the scissors.

135

THE HANDCUFFS

Strange as it may seem, this very simple trick puzzles a great many people.

Ask someone to tie your wrists together with a handkerchief, not too tightly. If you close your fists while the wrists are being tied, on opening them the handkerchief will be loose. Then get the assistant to pass a string between your two arms, to draw the two ends out in front of you, and to tie these two free ends together. The loop of the string will then be between your wrists and will be prevented from coming away by the handkerchief. Have your hands covered by a handkerchief and then proceed to remove the loop of string from your arms without undoing the handkerchief. To do this, work the fingers of your left hand between your wrists until you can grasp the loop of the string. Pull this forwards between your wrists and with your right hand pass it over the points of your left fingers and thumb and down the back of your hand.

It will then, of course, be free and can be pulled clear by the person holding the other end.

136

CHEATING THE HANGMAN

Put your head through the loop and let the string hang down in front of you. Hold the right string in the right hand, pass it to your left round the back of your neck and draw the loop down tight, showing the audience that the string is really round the neck. Take the left string in the right hand and draw it to the right side and slightly away from your body. At the same time take the right string in the left hand, draw it to the left and nearer to your body. Then with the thumbs and fingers of both hands grip the point where the two strings cross and allowing the long loop to hang down, pass this crossing over your head so that it rests on the back of the neck. Pull the pendant loop and the string will come away as if it had cut through your neck.

NETTING

A netting needle and a mesh stick are required. The needle should be made of thin hard wood about 7 or 8 inches long by $1\frac{1}{4}$ inches wide, shaped as shown in the illustration. The mesh stick is a piece of wood about 6 inches long by $1\frac{1}{2}$ inches wide by $\frac{3}{8}$ inch thick. The size of the mesh made will depend on the size of the mesh stick. Fill the needle with the string by winding it round the tine down into the hollow at the bottom of the needle, round the other side of the tine and back round the hollow, and so on until the needle is full. To make a fishing net proceed as follows :

Fig. 1.—First make a knotted loop in the string about the size of the mesh required and fix the end of the string to a hook or a nail in the wall.

Fig. 2.—Place the mesh stick *B* under the fall of the string, pass the needle under the stick and up through the loop from the back.

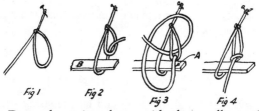

Fig. 3.—Draw the string down with the needle until the loop already made touches the mesh stick and with the left thumb hold the fall of the string down on to the mesh stick at the point *A*.

Fig. 4.—Throw a loop of the string over the back of the left hand and pass the needle behind the loop on the stick as shown. Draw the knot tight, releasing the left thumb as the knot tightens down.

Then remove the mesh stick, place it under the fall of the string as before, passing the string through the loop just made and knotting up as before. Continue until the net is sufficiently wide for your purpose. Then undo the first loop made as it will not be the proper size, pass a string through all the meshes, knot it in a loop and hang the net up on the hook by this loop. Then continue horizontally along all the meshes, but do not remove the mesh stick after making each loop, but work on it until it is full.

A fisherman's net of this type will have diagonal meshes when it is stretched out. Tennis nets having square meshes are made by machinery.

138
RING OFF THE STRING

1st.—Stand facing your assistant, who should hold his hands with the thumbs upright and palms facing each other.

2nd.—Thread a ring on to the loop of string and hang the ends of the loop over his upright thumbs, asking him to draw the string fairly taut. The ring should be near your assistant's right hand.

3rd.—Stand with your right shoulder opposite the assistant's left hand, thus facing his right hand, and place your two hands palms upwards above the two strings, your left hand in front of the near string and your right hand between the far string and the assistant's body. Your right hand should be between your body and your left hand.

4th.—With the fourth finger of the left hand cross above the near string and pick up from below the far string on the inside of the finger. Draw it above and across the near string, i.e., towards yourself. Then on the front of the fourth finger of the right hand pick up the near string from below, close to the assistant's left hand, and draw it away from you above the far string.

5th.—Transfer the loop on your left little finger to the assistant's left thumb, thus leaving your left hand free. With your left finger and thumb draw out the near string close to the assistant's right thumb, and hang the loop thus made over the assistant's left thumb.

6th.—Release your right little finger, pull on the ring, which will come away from the string.

There are other methods of doing this trick, some a good deal simpler to describe, but not any easier in practice. The trick is most effective in the above form.

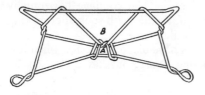

139

THE SEAGULL

This is a rather difficult figure and some digital skill is required in its construction.

1st.—Opening A.

2nd.—Pass the first fingers away from you over all the strings, then towards you under five strings and over the near thumb string. Pick up the near thumb string on the back of each forefinger, draw this string under all the others, bringing the hands up into the normal position by releasing the loops from the thumbs.

3rd.—Draw down the near lower first finger string with the front of the thumbs. Pass the thumbs under the far little finger string and draw this string to the front of the figure on the backs of the thumbs.

4th.—With the front of the thumbs draw the upper near first finger string down to the bottom of the figure, thus releasing the original thumb loops and keeping the tips of the thumbs pointing away from you.

5th.—Pass the thumbs away from you over the little finger string, and, turning them downwards and inwards, pick up this string on their backs and draw it towards you over the horizontal string at the bottom of the figure. Keep the thumbs still pointing downwards and the original thumb loops will slip off.

6th.—Each thumb will now be in a triangle. Turn the thumbs upwards and on their backs, pick up the top horizontal leg of these triangles, drawing the strings through to the front and bringing the hands up into the normal position.

7th.—Release the index fingers and draw the hands apart, when the figure as illustrated will be formed.

To release the figure, lay it down on your knees, place the fingers in the spaces *A* and *B*, and draw the two horizontal strings apart.

140

THE SPECTACLES

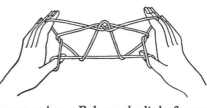

1st.—Opening A and release the thumbs.

2nd.—Pass the thumbs over two strings and pick up 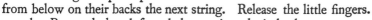 from below on their backs the next string.   Release the little fingers.

3rd.—Pass each thumb from below up into the index loops.

4th.—Navaho the thumb loops.

5th.—Pass each first finger down into the loops which have just been removed from the thumbs.   Extend by revolving the hands, thus letting the original index loops drop, lifting the index fingers upright, palms away from you and thumbs below.

A short string should be used for this figure.

141

THE RISING TIDE

1st.—Opening A.

2nd.—Pass the thumbs away from you over the far thumb string, under the next three strings and up into the little finger loop.

3rd.—With the backs of the thumbs pick up the far little finger string.   Turn the thumbs downwards, inwards and to the front, thus bringing the far little finger string to the front of the figure and the hands up into the normal position.

4th.—Put the thumbs up from below into the first finger loops.

5th.—Bend the little fingers towards you over two strings, and on their backs pick up from below the double far thumb strings.

6th.—Navaho the lowest loop on each little finger.

7th.—Lift off the single loops which run round each first finger and thumb, and drop them on the palmar side.   Extend, with fingers horizontal, thumbs pointing upwards, palms facing each other.

By twisting the wrists the tide may be made to rise and fall on the two pointed rocks.

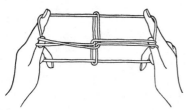

142

THE CATERPILLAR

The centre part of this figure is supposed to represent a caterpillar and as such is not very attractive. As, however, it can be made to crawl up and down in a very worm-like manner, it never fails to delight children. The construction is fairly easy, and is as follows :

1st.—Position one.

2nd.—With the right thumb and forefinger catch the near thumb string close to the left thumb, and loop it once anti-clockwise round the left thumb.

3rd.—Pick up this left thumb loop from the palmar side, on the back of the right forefinger and extend.

4th.—Put the left forefinger down into the right index loop and on its back pick up from below the right palmar string and extend.

5th.—Pick up the left palmar string in the same way by the back of the right index.

6th.—Remove the left hand from all the strings and turn the right hand palm downwards, fingers parallel with your body and with your thumb pointing towards you.

7th.—Lift up the loop which is nearest to the tip of your right forefinger and put it over the lower loop on the same finger, thus bringing it nearer to the base of that finger.

8th.—Bring the thumb and little finger of the left hand pointing towards you, in between the upper and lower far index finger strings, close to the index finger, and by separating them, pick up on the back of the little finger the lower far index string, and on the back of the thumb the upper far index string. Draw these loops off the index finger and extend.

9th.—Put the index fingers up from below into the thumb loops and release the thumbs.

10th.—Put the thumbs from above down into the index loops, picking up on their backs the far index strings, and release index fingers.

11th.—Bend the thumbs away from you over one string, and pick up on their backs the near little finger string.

12th.—The next movement is difficult to describe, and beginners sometimes find it difficult to do. Bend each index finger down under the far thumb string and with the back of its extreme tip pick up this string. Bring the index fingers upright, turning the palms away from you, thus raising the far thumb string to the top of the figure. At the same time grip this string by each thumb against the near inside of each index finger, thus holding it in place.

13th.—Draw the far little finger string down to the bottom of the figure by bending down the third and little fingers.

14th.—Draw the strings taut and hold the centre of the figure down flat on your knee. If the palms are turned upwards and then downwards the caterpillar will expand and contract, and by a little manipulation it may be made to crawl down your leg in a way which will delight all children and amuse many grown-ups.

To release this figure drop the right first finger and the left thumb and pull apart the loops on the left first finger and right thumb.

143

CUTTING THROUGH
THE TREE

1st.—Pass a cord twice round a tree as shown in Fig. 1.

2nd.—Stick a knife into the tree below the cord.

3rd.—Carry the right cord round the right side of the

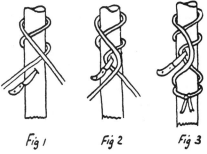

Fig 1   Fig 2   Fig 3

knife and over to the left, holding it in the left hand, and carry the left cord round the left side of the knife under the other cord and hold it in the right hand (Fig. 2). Then carry the two ends round the back of the tree, bring them to the front and tie in a knot (Fig. 3).

Remove the knife and the string will come away from the tree with the knot still intact. The right strand must always be on the top of the left one.

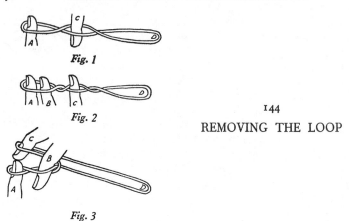

Fig. 1

Fig. 2

Fig. 3

144

REMOVING THE LOOP

This is probably the best and most mystifying of all the string releases. Hang one end of the loop on your assistant's forefinger *A*, which must be held upright and straight, and pull the string taut and horizontal by placing the forefinger of your left hand into the other end of the loop at *D*. Bring your right hand palm downwards, thumb towards you, above the two strings and in line with your left shoulder. With the inside of your right middle finger *C* pick up the left-hand string from the left side and draw it to the right above the right string (Fig. 1).

Push the middle finger down between the two strings and bring it pointing upwards by a clockwise turn, thus picking up the right string (which was to the left) on the thumb side of the middle finger. There are now two crosses on the string. Slide the right hand towards your assistant and insert the right forefinger *B* (Fig. 2) from the right side and from below up into the loop close to his finger. Give the hand a counter-clockwise half turn, thus bringing the fingers pointing downwards and causing the right forefinger to pick up the strings on its sides. Raise the middle finger *C* up, turn it to the right and place its tip on the tip of your assistant's finger (Fig. 3). Release your first finger and the loop round the finger of your assistant will come away.

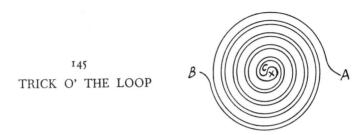

145
TRICK O' THE LOOP

This is a very old swindle usually worked at country fairs by three-card men and thimble-riggers for the purpose of parting the unwary from their money.

A leather strap or a piece of webbing about an inch wide is folded apparently in the middle and made into a flat spiral on the table, as shown in the illustration, but with the coils close together. The game is to find the centre of the loop. The operator gives a pointed stick to his victim and offers to bet that he will not be able to find the centre. When the stick is pushed down into the centre the operator pulls the ends *A* and *B* together, thus uncoiling the spiral. No matter where the player places the point he cannot win. If he places it at *C*, when the ends *A* and *B* are pulled it will, of course, not be in the centre. If he actually does place it in the centre *X* the operator gives part *A* another turn, which has the effect of bringing it outside part *B*. When the two ends are pulled the point will be on the outside, so that the player always loses his money. The operator generally makes an extra small turn in the centre when he starts coiling up the spiral, to make it seem more difficult to find the centre.

This trick may be shown by doubling a strip of paper nearly in the centre, placing a pencil in the fold and rolling the strip round it with the short end outwards. An extra turn with the long end will bring the pencil to the outside of the fold when the paper is unrolled.

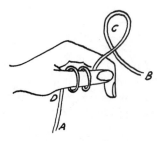

146

THREADING THE NEEDLE

Take a piece of thick string about 3 feet long and, starting about 9 inches from end A, make a few anti-clockwise turns round the left thumb, ending inside the thumb and gripping end A by the fingers of the left hand. Then throw a small loop on the end B, making sure that the part $B\ C$ is behind the string leaving the thumb. Grip the crossing of $B\ C$ between the thumb and first finger, and grip the end B between the second and third fingers. Release part A from the fingers of the left hand and hold it between the thumb and forefinger of the right hand close to the end. Explain to your audience that you are going to pass A through the loop so quickly that they will not see how it is done. Make a few feints with the point of the string and then push it quickly to the left, making sure that the part D close to the thumb runs between the left finger and thumb and up the front of B. The part A will then be in the loop C and it will look as if it had been passed through from the front. You can now pull the end A out of the loop and give two or three more demonstrations. The second demonstration is usually the most convincing, as the spectators see the string actually removed from the loop and mysteriously threaded again.

It is necessary to make at least six turns round the thumb. If you make only two or three, as shown in the illustration, the audience will notice that each time you thread the needle a turn is lost off the thumb.

This trick is said to be used as a password by a tribe of Indians living in the North West of Canada.

147

THE FENCE

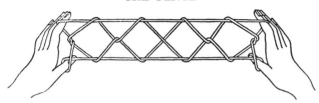

1st.—Opening A and release the thumbs.

2nd.—Pass the thumbs under all the strings and on their backs pick up from below the far fourth string and draw it to the front of the figure.

3rd.—Pass the thumbs over one string, and on their backs pick up the far index string.

4th.—Release the little fingers, pass them over one string, and on their backs pick up the far thumb string. Release the thumbs.

5th.—Bend the thumbs over two strings and pick up the near little finger string.

6th.—Put the thumbs up into the index loops close to the fingers.

7th.—Navaho the thumb loops.

8th.—Put the index fingers down into the small triangles close to the thumbs, release little fingers, revolve the hands away from you, palms outwards, thumbs downwards, and index fingers upright. One loop will drop off each index finger, thus completing the figure shown. A fairly short string should be used for this figure. To break up this figure pull the horizontal strings apart. During the weaving of this figure the strings should be kept loose.

KNOTS, BENDS AND SPLICES

THE ART OF MAKING KNOTS AND BENDS

It is extraordinary how little the average individual knows about the art of making even the simplest knots. String is so cheap in these days that it probably does not matter much if the knots are so made that the string has to be cut because it cannot be undone. Nevertheless, knots made in a haphazard way generally slip, always jamb in their turns, and are never so good for their intended purposes as properly made knots and bends. On shipboard, where rope is a very heavy item of expense, great care is taken to see that all knots are scientifically made, not only that they may serve their purpose as knots in the most efficient manner, but to ensure that they may be readily undone, and that during their life they will damage the rope as little as possible. Knots which jamb or work and chafe are never used at sea, and every knot is designed so that it will serve its purpose with the smallest number of parts.

Look at the next parcel you receive from your draper. It will be tied with a thin string bent together at the ends in a most unholy tangle of slip knots which must be cut before the parcel can be opened. All these kinks and turns are necessary because each one is inefficient, but it is obvious that the whole *mélange* cannot make the parcel more secure than the strength of the string will allow. A single reef knot, which is stronger than the string on which it is made, will tie the parcel more securely and can be undone with the greatest ease without damaging the string. The art of knotting is one of the oldest, and nearly all the knots and bends in use at the present day have been handed down from the very earliest times. In this section most of the knots and bends in general use are illustrated and are self-explanatory. A few fancy knots are shown to introduce the subject to those interested.

Notes are added where the method of tying or the use of the knot is not clearly conveyed by the illustrations.

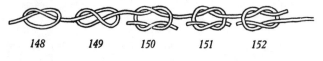

148   149   150   151   152

148
OVERHAND KNOT

149
FIGURE OF EIGHT KNOT

150
REEF KNOT

151
GRANNIE KNOT

This is an unsatisfactory knot, as it will slip and jamb. It is therefore never used except by those who do not know how to make the equally simple reef knot.

152
TOM FOOL KNOT

This knot, which cannot be made overhand, is used by sailors to tie up their belongings. They can tell if the parcel has been opened by a person who is not familiar with the knot, as anyone re-tying the parcel is sure to use an ordinary reef knot, which is so similar.

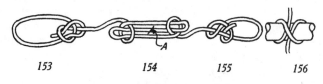

153   154   155   156

153
BOWLINE

This is a very cleverly designed knot which can neither slip nor jamb, and may be undone very easily.

154
SHEEP SHANK

Used for shortening a rope. It is sometimes called the escaping prisoner's knot, as the middle strand *A* may be cut and still bear the weight on the fall. When the prisoner has climbed down to the bottom, a shake of the rope will cause the hitches to come adrift and most of the rope will fall to the ground.

155	156
RUNNING BUNTLINE	CLOVE HITCH

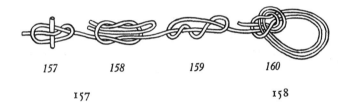

157   158   159   160

157	158
MARLINE-SPIKE HITCH	BOW REEF KNOT

159
STEVEDORE'S KNOT

160
BOWLINE ON A BIGHT
(or Boatswain's Seat)

This is made by throwing a hitch on the bight, passing the doubled part through it, then down over itself and up as shown, where it locks the hitch.

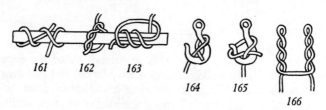

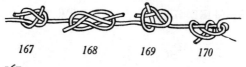

161
ROLLING HITCH

This is a clove hitch with an extra turn.

162
TIMBER HITCH

163
TOPSAIL SPAR BEND

164
BLACKWALL HITCH

165
MIDSHIPMAN HITCH

166
CATSPAW

167
SHEET BEND

168
CARRICK BEND

169
WEAVER'S KNOT

170
TOPSAIL SHEET BEND

A very secure bend.

171   172   173

171
TRUE LOVER'S KNOT

Made by forming a clove hitch and passing the loops through each other. Also known as the handcuff knot, as it is often used to tie the wrists together.

172
PLAIT KNOT

Used for shortening a rope.

First loop up the rope as shown at the left of the illustration to the length required. Lay 1 over 2 then 3 over 1 and under 2 and so on, dipping the end of 3 through the loop as necessary.

173
CHAIN KNOT

This is another and quicker method of rope-shortening.

First make an overhand knot, but instead of passing the end through, form a bight only. Then pass the fall through from the back, thus forming another bight. Continue to the length necessary, finally passing the end through the last bight, thus stopping off the chain. To undo, remove the last hitch and pull on the end of the rope.

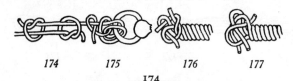

174   175   176   177

174
SIMPLE SHROUD KNOT

This knot was used for quickly repairing the shrouds in men-of-war after they had been shot away. A proper shroud knot is made by unstranding the two ends of the rope for a short distance, marrying them together and forming first a wall knot with the lower strands round the upper rope and then another wall knot with the upper strands round the lower rope.

175
ANCHOR OR FISHERMAN'S BEND

176
WALL KNOT

This knot is made by undoing the strands for a short distance, passing each strand under the next one as shown and then pulling all three strands up tight. A double wall knot is made by following each strand round a second time.

177
CROWN KNOT

This knot, similar to a wall knot, is made by passing each strand over the next one. Double and triple crown knots are made by following the strands round two or three times. Wall and crown knots are often combined by making first, a wall, and then crowning it.

178
MATTHEW WALKER KNOT

This knot is the same as a wall except that each strand passes under the next two and then up through its own bight.

179
SHROUD KNOT
(See 174)

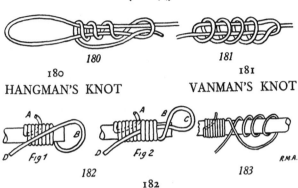

180   181
180   181
HANGMAN'S KNOT   VANMAN'S KNOT

182   183
182
WHIPPING A ROPE

First.—Lay the end *A* along the rope and whip until well secured.

Second.—Lay the other end of the whipping cord along the part already whipped, holding it in place with the left thumb (Fig. 1).

Third.—Continue the whipping with the part *B*, throwing the loop *C* over the end of the rope at each turn (Fig. 2).

Fourth.—Pull on end *D* until the loop *B C* is drawn tight.

182A

In the American whipping the ends *A* and *D* are brought out at same place and then tied with a reef knot.

183
WHIPPING A FISHING ROD

Proceed as in whipping a rope's end, but when you have done sufficient take a few loose back turns as shown and put the long end under the last ordinary turn. Then finish the whipping until all the back turns are out. Pull out the long end through the last turns.

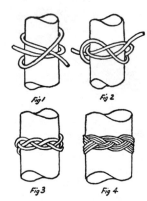

184
TURK'S HEAD

Fig. 1.—Make a clove hitch round the article to be ornamented.

Fig. 2.—Pass one end over and under each turn all the way round.

Fig. 3.—Continue passing the ends over and under in turn.

Fig. 4.—Follow the lay round, passing the ends under and over evenly as often as desired.

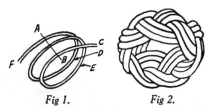

Fig 1.   Fig 2.

185
TURK'S HEAD OR BRACELET

When the Turk's Head can be fitted after it is made, to the article it is to ornament, the easiest method is to first make two bights in the middle of the rope as shown at Fig. 1 and seize all the three cords temporarily at $A\,B$. Then plait together parts $C\,D$ and E, passing D and E through from side to side and dipping end C when necessary. Carry this right round and remove seizing from $A\,B$. Then follow this lead round with F and C as many times as required, finishing off the ends by tucking them under. Fig. 2 shows a three-part Turk's Head.

186
FISHING LINE KNOT

Knot No. 174 is used by fishermen to tie lengths of gut together. The knot is a very secure one which does not waste any of the gut.

187

SLINGING A BARREL

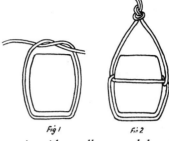

Fig 1   Fig 2

Stand the barrel on the middle of a short piece of rope. Pass the two ends up the sides of the barrel and make a knot as shown in Fig. 1. Then pull one part towards you and place it across the barrel about two-thirds of the way up. Pass the other part down on the opposite side, pull up and bend the two ends together as shown in Fig. 2.

188

SHORT SPLICE

Unlay the ends of the two ropes and marry them together as shown in the figure.

Then pass each strand over across one strand of the opposite rope and tuck it under the next strand. Do this to all three strands and then a second or third time. Harden well down into place. If a neat splice is required, taper the strands off after the second tuck.

189

EYE SPLICE

Unlay the strands at one end of the rope and lay them on the standing part to the size of eye required. Pass a marlin spike under one of the strands of the standing part and pass one of the unlaid strands into the space left when the spike is withdrawn. Do the same with the other two strands, and follow round two or three times, tapering off if a neat-looking splice is required.

190

SERVING THE HANDLE OF A
HOT WATER JUG

Take a piece of string of the necessary length and cut it into two pieces, one piece being double the length of the other. Put a thumb knot on one end of the short piece and form a clove hitch in the middle of the longer piece round one end of the part to be whipped. Tuck the short piece under the clove hitch and tighten down. The clove hitch will hold the short piece and the thumb knot will prevent it slipping out during the whipping. You now have three strings fastened at one end of the handle. Pass one string round the handle and make a half hitch, bringing the crossing to the front of the handle. Draw it tight in the direction in which the hitch was made. With the second string make a similar half hitch round the handle in the opposite direction and with the third string make a half hitch in the same direction as the first one. Render all the cords up tight and touching each other. Keep on making half hitches in the same order, so that the handle will be tightly whipped on the inside and ornamented with a three-part plait down the outside. Finish off by tucking the ends under.

191

THE SANDAL KNOT OF THE ANCIENTS

The ancients evidently suffered from their sandal strings becoming undone, so they invented the sandal knot which is in use to this day in the mountainous parts of middle Europe.

First make an ordinary double bow knot and draw it tight. Then pass the right bow through the left one and pull the end of the part running to the left bow, which will tighten the outside bow on to the neck of the inner one. The two ends will be uneven in length, exactly as shown on the ancient statues. To undo the knot pull the part going to the inner bow.

192

DIAMOND KNOT

Fig. 1.—Start by throwing down a loop on *A*. Then throw a second loop and place it under the first one.

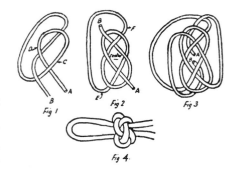

Fig. 2.—Pass *B* under *A*, over *C*, under its own part and over *D*, thus making Fig. 2.

Fig. 3.—Pass *A* over *F* under the three parts shown and up through the centre diamond space. Then pass end *B* over *E* under three parts and up through the centre space, thus making Fig. 3.

Fig. 4.—Draw out *A* and *B* and render up the turns, thus making Fig. 4.

193

LONG SPLICE

Unlay the strands at the end of each rope about twelve times the diameter of the rope, and marry the strands together as in a short splice. Put a temporary seizing on if required, to hold the centre of the splice together. Then unlay one strand still further, laying into the vacant space the corresponding strand of the other rope. Do the same on the opposite side.

There will then be a long and short strand at each end and two long strands in the middle. Cut off the strands so as to make them all the same length and then tie them together with the lay of the rope. Tuck all six ends in as in a short splice, tapering off the strands as required. Harden down well into place with a mallet, but do not cut off the end of the strands too short until the splice has settled down into place.

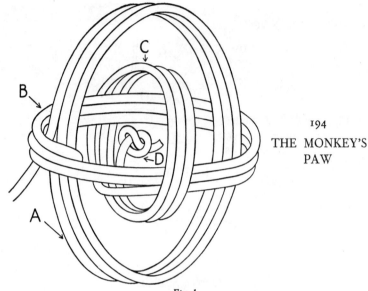

194

THE MONKEY'S
PAW

Fig. 1

Fig. 2

This knot is made by taking three turns of the rope round the hand as shown at A in Fig. 1, and then three turns B at right angles to A. Then three more complete turns C are made on the outside of B and inside A. A thumb knot D is made on the end of the rope and tucked into the centre of all the turns. Then holding this thumb knot between the first finger and thumb of the left hand draw the turns back one at a time, thus enclosing the thumb knot in the centre. Gradually work all the turns backwards until they are quite tight when the finished knot will be as shown in Fig. 2.

If the knot is immersed in water it will be impossible to undo it.

GAMES FOR THE AGILE

195
LIFTING A CHAIR

Lay a chair down on its back on the floor.
Grasp one of the legs by its extreme end, lift
the chair bodily, turn it up and set it on its
legs again. Then place it down again, lay a
book on the back of the chair and try once
more.

196
KNOCKING OVER THE CORK

Place a cork on the table. Stand 10 feet away. Take three paces
forward, then close one eye and try to push the cork over with your
finger.

197
SMASHING THE MATCH-BOX

Balance the empty tray of a match-box on its outside
case as shown in the illustration. Ask a strong man to
try to smash the box with a fair blow of his fist.

198
TEST OF BALANCE

Look at your feet through the wrong end of a pair of opera glasses and walk down the room, putting heel to toe alternately, along a seam in the carpet or along a piece of string stretched across the floor.

199
BOTTLING THE CORK

Lay an empty wine bottle on its side on the table and place a small cork just inside its mouth. Try to blow the cork into the bottle. This may be done by blowing through a straw on to the end of the small cork.

200

HOUDIN'S MEMORY GAME

Place a number of small objects, such as coins, pencils, chessmen, etc.—about twenty-five in all—on a large tray, and cover them over with a cloth. Place the tray on the middle of the table and let the players all stand round so that they have a full view of the tray. The cloth should be removed from the tray for a few seconds and then covered up again. The players are given three minutes to write down as many objects as they can remember. The winner is the person who makes the most complete and correct list.

201

PUTTING A BROOMSTICK OVER YOUR BACK

Grasp a broomstick with the two hands about 3 feet apart and hold it horizontally, palms upwards. Lean down and place the left end of the stick behind the left leg. Lift the left foot and pass the middle of the stick under the foot from back to front. Then pass the stick over the head, **down** the back, under the right foot and so back to the original position.

202

LAYING DOWN THE CORK

Toe a line. Bend the knees and holding a cork in the right hand, place this hand and arm behind the right leg. Then lay the cork down as far as you can in front of the line, recovering your position without touching the ground with your hands. The winner is the person who lays the cork the greatest distance from the line.

203

TRIAL OF STRENGTH

Place the palm of your hand on the crown of your head and ask someone to lift it off by pressing up your forearm from below.

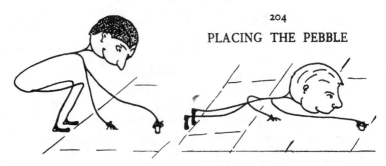

204
PLACING THE PEBBLE

Toe a line. Stoop forward on your toes, putting the palm of your left hand on the ground, thus supporting the body but not letting the knees touch the ground. With the right hand place the pebble as far away from the line as you can and regain an upright position without moving the left hand along the ground, *i.e.*, with a clear spring. The person who places the pebble furthest from the line is the winner.

It is possible to place the pebble a great deal further out by the following trick, which does not infringe the rules laid down. Put the left hand down as before, but at such a distance that you can easily recover the upright position, *i.e.*, only moderately far from the line. Then straighten out your legs, thus bringing the toes some way behind the line. Lower the body by bending the left arm until the chest is resting on the back of the left hand and with the right hand place the pebble at full arm's length in front of the line. Press the body up by straightening the left arm, bring the toes up to the line and recover the upright position. It will be found that the pebble can be placed at least 12 inches further away by this trick.

205
BLOWING OVER A SIXPENNY PIECE[*]

Lay the coin down on the table cloth. You can blow it over on to the reverse side by holding the left hand, palm towards you, about 6 inches behind the coin and resting on the table. If you blow in front of the coin it will turn over quite easily.

---

*Or use a quarter or half dollar.

206
THE PEBBLE ON THE SHOVEL

Hold a wide-mouthed navvy's shovel horizontally in front of your body with the left hand near the iron end and the right hand on the handle. Place a small pebble in the middle of the shovel and with an upward movement of the left hand throw it towards your body, letting it fall down in the space between your arms and the handle of the shovel. Then with a quick circular movement of both hands horizontally and clockwise try to catch the pebble before it reaches the ground. Look out for your shins !

207
ROUND THE BROOM-STICK

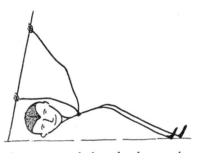

Grip a broomstick, holding it horizontal, with the left hand palm upwards about 8 inches from the left end, and with the right hand palm downwards about 3 feet from the left hand. Then turn the stick into the vertical position and plant the short end at the left hand firmly on the ground. To do this you will have to bring your body approximately horizontal and parallel to the ground, your weight being supported by your arms and your legs stretched out straight. Turn over with your back to the ground, bring your head between the ground and your left arm, work your head and body round to the other side, thus facing the ground with the body still horizontal. Continue thus, eventually gaining an upright position. No part of the body except the feet may touch the ground during the game. Practice this game on the lawn and do not attempt it on a polished floor.

208

GYROSCOPIC PRECESSION

Hold a bicycle wheel vertically, *i.e.*, in its normal running position, by gripping the ball-bearing spindles at both ends between the thumb and forefinger of each hand. With the second finger of the right hand spin the wheel at a fair speed by pressing on the spokes near the hub. Remove the left hand from the spindle and the wheel will remain balanced on the forefinger of the right hand. It will gradually precess towards the arm. Before it touches transfer the weight to the forefinger of the left hand by placing the tip of the finger under the other end of the spindle. It will then precess in the opposite direction and may be transferred again to the right forefinger.

209

PICKING UP THE PIN

Push a pin a short way into the seat of a chair on its left side (right when sitting in the chair). Sit down on the chair. Then turn your body to your left and bend round the back of the chair, remove the pin with your teeth and get back again into a sitting position on the chair. You must not touch the ground (you probably will), and your legs must remain on the chair.

210

THE TALL HAT

Ask someone to point out with a walking stick on the skirting board of the room the height he thinks a tall hat is. Then bring in a hat and see if he has judged the height correctly.

211

LIGHTING THE CANDLE

Lay a magnum bottle or a jar on its side on the ground. Sit on it with its axis in line with your body, your legs straight out in front of you, your right heel on the ground, and your left heel on the toe of the right foot. Lift a match-box from the ground on your left, open it, strike a match and light a candle placed on the ground on your right.

212

THE VACUUM

Hold the left hand horizontally, fingers together, palm downwards, thumb nearest to your body. With the right hand place a piece of paper about $3\frac{1}{2}$ inches square up against your palm. Then blow strongly through the space between your second and third fingers, at the same time removing your right hand which was supporting the paper against the palm. The harder you blow the tighter the paper will adhere to the palm. Cease blowing and the paper will fall to the ground.

213

ANOTHER VACUUM EXPERIMENT

Fill a tumbler with water (quite full) and place a sheet of stiff writing paper over the mouth of the tumbler so as to exclude all air. Put the left hand on the sheet of paper, hold it down in place and invert the tumbler. Remove the left hand, when it will be found that the water will not run out.

214

THE NEWSPAPER

Lay a newspaper down on the ground so that two persons standing on it cannot shake hands with each other. To do this put it across the doorstep and shut the door, leaving one person outside.

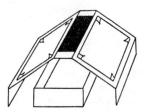

215
BLOWING A MATCH-BOX
BACKWARDS

Open out the case of a match-box and lay it down as shown. Lay the empty tray down in front and blow it through the tunnel from front to back. Then place the hand as in No. 205 ; blow against the open palm and the tray will come towards you through the tunnel.

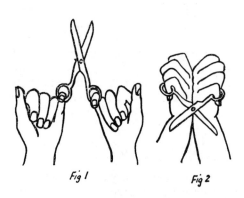

Fig 1

Fig 2

216
REVOLVING THE
SCISSORS

Loop a pair of scissors over the two little fingers and let them hang down as shown in Fig. 1. Rock them slightly to and fro as a pendulum, and then turn them up, points facing away from you, then points upright, then towards you, down, and round again until the points are facing you, as shown in Fig. 2. The points of the scissors will, during this turn, have made about one revolution and three-quarters. Very few persons will be able to bring the scissors round more than one revolution. The secret lies in the fact that it is impossible to bring the points into the position shown in Fig. 2 unless the loops of the scissors are placed between the tips and the first joint of the little fingers. Nearly everyone will put their fingers farther into the loops, thus making it quite impossible to get the points to come up to the position shown.

217

THE CARD BRIDGE

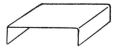

Bend a visiting card down at right angles about half an inch from each short end to form a bridge. Lay it down on the table on the two bent edges and try to blow it over on its back.

The secret is to blow down on the table about 8 or 10 inches in front of the card.

218

PICKING UP THE CORK

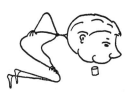

Kneel down and place a cork upright in front of you about 18 inches away. Clasp your hands behind your back and try to pick up the cork with your teeth. Mind your nose ! ! !

219

SPHEROIDAL STATE OF WATER

If an iron spoon is made red hot and a drop of water is placed in it, the water will not boil at first, but will dance about on the top of a layer of steam. When the spoon has cooled sufficiently the water will make contact with the iron and suddenly go off in a puff of steam.

220

THE CANDLE AND FUNNEL

Place a candle in front of a funnel and try to extinguish it by blowing down the small end of the funnel. You can only do this if you lower the funnel until the top edge of the large end is in line with the flame of the candle.

221

SKITTLES

Lay down three cotton reels on their ends on the floor in a line (like wickets), and at such distance apart that a tennis ball will just barely pass through between either pair. Put a penny on the top of each reel and bet at a penny a shot that the players cannot knock more than one over by rolling the ball from a distance of about 10 feet, the players to win the coins they knock over if they succeed in knocking off more than one at a time. This is the story which the showman tells at country fairs when he is working this profitable game.

"Roll the ball, bowl the ball, hinch the ball, pitch the ball, any way you tumble or toss; two of the coins or two of the sticks, I don't care which. You're sure to win."

222

THE SQUEAKER

A wide blade of grass held and tightly stretched as shown at *A* between the two thumbs with its edge to the front will squeak if the mouth is placed against the thumbs and a strong current of air is blown through the hollow space between the thumbs. The lips should be touching the thumbs.

223

COCK FIGHTING

In this game two players sit down on their haunches, each with a broomstick placed between their arms and their hocks and with their hands clasped in front of their knees. They then hop about the floor and try to knock each other over. Plenty of room and no valuable furniture within reach is advisable when this game is being played.

SECTION EIGHT

TOYS

224
KINEMATOGRAPH

DRAW a series of pictures on the bottom right-hand corners of the leaves of a book. By riffling the leaves over with the thumb of the right hand the pictures will become animated if they have been drawn in steps like a kinematograph. A girl skipping is a simple example, or two boxers or boys on a see-saw work very well. To get a good result it is important to draw the figures on exactly the same relative area on each leaf. A series of V's and straight lines to represent a flying bird works very well or an aeroplane dropping bombs is easily drawn. A set of two dots may be made to collide and fly apart and innumerable designs may be worked out by ingenious youths.

225
DOVETAIL PUZZLE

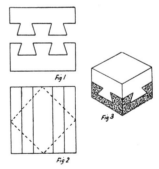

Two pieces of wood, one boxwood and the other ebony, are joined together so as to show a dovetail on all four faces. The easiest method to construct this puzzle is to make two dovetails in two cubes of wood in the ordinary way and then to plane off the corners as shown by the dotted lines so as to make a square having a diagonal equal to the sides of the original square. The pieces should be glued together before the four edges are planed off. If the bottom piece is hollowed out and filled with lead the puzzle makes a very useful paperweight.

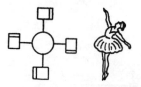

226

THE DANCER

Push two needles through a small cork at right angles to each other and on the ends of the needles stick four small squares of cork. To the four faces of the square fix small pieces of camphor, mount a cardboard figure in the centre on a pin and put the whole outfit into a basin of water. The dancers will revolve merrily until the water becomes contaminated. Use a large basin and pure camphor.

227

SQUARE PEG IN A ROUND HOLE

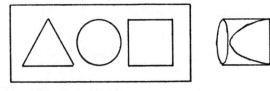

The illustration shows a board having round, square and triangular holes cut in it, and a plug to fit all three. The plug is a cylinder the same diameter as the round hole, its length equal to the sides of the square hole, and has the corners shaved off to fit into the triangular hole. All three holes must be the same height and the base of the triangle must be equal to the diameter of the circular hole.

228

BLOWING A CANDLE FLAME TOWARDS YOU

Hold a card between yourself and a candle and blow against the card. The flame will be drawn towards the card.

229

VACUUM AND PRESSURE

Take a cotton reel and make a cardboard disc about the same diameter. Punch three holes in the disc and with three pins mount it on the reel as shown. The holes should be an easy fit on the pins, and the pins should be upright so that when the reel is held vertically the disc will fall by gravity down on to the heads of the pins. Hold the reel vertically with the disc underneath. Push the disc up until it touches the reel. Then try to blow the disc away from the reel by blowing down the hole and at the same time removing the finger. The harder you blow the tighter will the disc stick to the reel.

One pin only in the centre of the disc is almost as good.

230

THE STRING AXLE

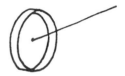

Punch a small hole from the outside in the lid of a tin cannister about 3 inches in diameter and pass a string through the hole with a knot on the outside of the lid. By running along a smooth pavement and holding the string at about the angle shown the lid can be rolled along at a high rate.

231

THE SUCKER

Make a disc of leather about 3 inches in diameter and $\frac{1}{8}$ inch thick. Pierce a small hole in the centre of the disc and pass a thin string through it, fastening it with a small knot underneath. Wet the leather and stick it down on a wet smooth pavement. The average small boy will be unable to pull it upwards away from the stone.

232
THE DIVER

Blow a small glass bulb with a capillary opening in the stem. The weight should be so adjusted that the bulb will just float stem downwards when placed in water. Put the bulb into a thin 16-ounce medicine bottle quite full of water, and cork tightly. Be careful not to burst the bottle. Hold the bottle in the hand, press the sides inwards and the bulb will sink to the bottom. By releasing the pressure it will rise to the top again. You can therefore make it rise and fall at " the word of command " in what seems to be a most mysterious manner.

233
BUZZER

Make a cardboard disc about 2 inches in diameter and rather thick. Make two holes in the disc equidistant from the centre, and thread a closed loop through them as shown. Place the thumbs through the loops A and B and by giving one hand a circular motion, twist up the cord a few times. Pull the hands apart, which will cause the disc to revolve. Bring them together again as the disc reverses. After a little practice the disc can be spun at a very high speed and will give out a loud buzzing sound.

The sound can be increased slightly by notching the edge of the disc.

234
THE SNORER

Take a plain piece of wood about 8 inches long by 2 inches wide and ¼ inch thick. With a knife notch the edges all round. Make a hole in one end and fasten a piece of string through this hole. Hold the end of the string and revolve the snorer at arm's length in a vertical circle. It will give out a very weird moaning sound, similar to that which a Banshee ought to make.

235

THE MYSTERIOUS TOP

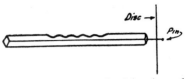

This very ingenious toy can be made from a rod of hardwood about 9 inches long by ⅜ inch square. Form four or five smooth indentations on one edge of the square as shown. Drive a pin into one end to act as the axis of the disc. Then make a disc about 2 inches in diameter from a lady's visiting card with a hole in the centre the size of the head of the pin. Hold the stick upright in the left hand with the notches towards you, and place the disc on the pin. If you stroke the stick with a pencil held horizontally in the right hand up and down across the notches, the disc will rotate at a very high speed. By holding the first finger of the right hand up against the side of the stick the disc can be made to rotate in the opposite direction. If the notches are well proportioned the disc can be made to rotate and reverse at will by stroking the notches with the fingers of the right hand thus: Hold the stick upright with the notches pointing slightly towards your right. Stroke the notches up and down with the nail of your second finger and rub the side of your first finger against the plain left side of the stick. This will start the disc revolving. Then turn the stick slightly in your left hand so as to bring the notches pointing to the left and stroke the notches with the nail of your first finger, holding the second finger against the right side of the stick. The disc will soon stop and then start revolving in the opposite direction.

The onlookers cannot see that you have made any change and are very mystified when you make the disc stop and reverse at the word of command.

236

RADISH SUCKER

A large radish, if cut in two across its greatest diameter, will lift a wet plate if the cut face is hollowed out slightly.

237
STROBOSCOPIC DISC

Make a disc for the mysterious top and with ink draw on it the pattern shown. This pattern must be laid out accurately with compasses, and may be tinted in various colours. If this disc is revolved in the light of an electric lamp which is connected to the alternating current mains, very pretty stroboscopic effects will be obtained, the various sets of points stopping and sometimes going backwards as the speed rises and falls.

The best effect is obtained by illuminating the disc by means of a neon lamp. One type known as the Osglim lamp, which is used as a nightlight, gives in a darkened room plenty of light for the purpose.

Many other pattern discs can be made. Colour top designs are very effective. For example, make an eight-pointed star and paint it red. You will then get a colour from red gradually turning to white at the edges, or you can paint the points of the star blue and the spaces yellow.

238
FIXING CANDLES TO A CHRISTMAS TREE

Unless the candles on a Christmas tree are fixed vertically they do not burn well and drip wax on the floor. A simple way to fix them to

the tree is to make small bent-wire hooks thus :

Heat the short part of the hook, stick the candle on to it and fasten a counterweight on to the long end as shown in the illustration. The counterweight may be made from a walnut or from any of the small ornaments used to decorate the tree. If the hook is hung over the branch the candle will stand upright even when the branch is inclined.

Christmas trees are now usually illuminated by electric lamps, which are much more effective, but not much safer unless the lamps are fed from a wireless accumulator or motor-car battery.

239

CAMPHOR BOAT

Make a boat as shown in the illustration out of a flat piece of thin wood. Place a piece of camphor in the hollow at the stern so that it will just touch the water when the boat is floated. The boat will sail round a tub of water if the camphor is arranged a little to one side so as to act as a rudder.

240

BALANCING A COIN ON THE EDGE OF A TUMBLER

Put a half-crown* between the tines of two dinner forks as shown in the illustration and lay the side of the coin on the edge of a tumbler. With a little adjustment the whole outfit may be balanced quite securely.

241

THE SPINNING AEROPLANE

Cut a strip of paper 12 inches long and $\frac{1}{2}$ inch wide. Fold it in the centre and twist the doubled end on itself for 3 or 4 inches. Then turn the two single ends outwards so that the paper is in Y form. If this is dropped from a height it will spin very rapidly as it falls to the ground.

*Or use a quarter for this trick.

242
THE COLUMBUS EGG

Make a small hole in the side of a hen's egg and empty the contents with a blowpipe. When the interior is dry put in some fine sand until the egg is quarter full and seal up the hole with white wax. The egg may then be balanced in any position. Take another egg, and after emptying it, put in some small shot and a few pieces of wax. Hold the egg upright and heat gently over a gas flame. The wax will melt and stick the shot to the bottom, so that when the egg is placed on the table it will always stand upright, owing to the fact that the centre of gravity is near the lower end.

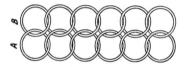

243
A JACOB'S LADDER

Make about three dozen rings about an inch in diameter by winding a piece of wire round a rod to form a spiral and then cutting through each turn. Join the rings up as shown in the illustration. By holding ring *A* and dropping *B* and *vice versâ*, the dropped ring will appear to fall from the top to the bottom.

PROBLEMS

Answers to the problems in this section are given on pp. 154–155.

CROSS WORD

HERE is a cross word which reads the same in four different ways.
Try to discover others.

```
S  A  T  O  R
A  R  E  P  O
T  E  N  E  T
O  P  E  R  A
R  O  T  A  S
```

ALPHABET SENTENCE

Here is a sentence which contains all the letters of the alphabet.
Try to make up others :

" Pack my box with five dozen liquor jugs."

The quick brown fox jumped over the lazy dogs tail

THE DRUNKARD

At one time the Mexican and the American dollar were at a discount
of 10 cents on opposite sides of the border. A man goes into a
public house on the Mexican side, buys 10 cents' worth of beer and
tenders a Mexican dollar in payment. He receives an American
dollar as his change. He then crosses the border to the American
side, buys another 10 cent drink, tenders his American dollar and
gets a Mexican dollar as change. He finishes the day dead drunk
with his original dollar in his pocket. Who pays for the drinks ?

247

STRIKING CLOCK

If a clock takes 8 seconds to strike eight how many seconds will it take to strike twelve ?

If it takes 6 seconds to strike six, how many seconds will it take to strike twelve ?

248

DIVINING A NUMBER

Ask someone to write down any three different digits, say—

	3 2 6
Then to reverse them	6 2 3
Then to take the difference	2 9 7

Then ask him what his last digit is and you will be able to tell him the result. In this trick the middle number is always nine and the first and last digits together equal nine. If therefore you are told the last digit you can find the first one.

249

PLURAL NOUN

A noun there is of plural number,
A foe to ease and peaceful slumber.
Now any other noun you take
By adding " s " you plural make,
But if you add an " s " to this
Strange is the metamorphosis.
Plural is plural now no more,
And sweet what bitter was before.

250

CAT AND RATS

If a cat and a half can kill a rat and a half in a minute and a half, how long will it take one cat to kill 60 rats ?

251

Ask someone to write down quickly ELEVEN THOUSAND ELEVEN HUNDRED AND ELEVEN.

252

TRAIN SPEED

What part of a train, travelling at 50 miles per hour forwards, is moving backwards at about 10 miles per hour ?

253

CHOOSE YOUR ANSWER

Write down the figures 1 to 9 in a row, omitting the figure 8, and multiply it by any multiple of 9, say 3 × 9 = 27 thus :

```
      1 2 3 4 5 6 7 9
                  2 7
      ─────────────────
        8 6 4 1 9 7 5 3
      2 4 6 9 1 3 5 8
      ─────────────────
      3 3 3 3 3 3 3 3 3
      ─────────────────
```

If you multiply the row by any other multiple of nine, say 6 × 9 = 54 the answer will come out all sixes.

254
REVERSED NUMBERS

Take any three different numbers	5 2 1
Reverse them	1 2 5
	———
The difference is	3 9 6
Reverse this difference	6 9 3
	———
The sum will always be	1 0 8 9
	———

If you try this with £ s. d. less than £12 the answer will always be £12 18s. 11d.

255
CRICKET AVERAGE

Two bowlers during the season have each taken 28 wickets for 60 runs. One bowler in the next match takes 4 wickets for 36 runs, and the other takes 1 wicket for 27 runs. Which has now the best average?

256
MY FATHER'S SON

This is the problem the discussions on which have separated families.

A person looking at a portrait said :

"Sisters and brothers have I none,
But that man's father was my father's son."

What relation was the speaker to the subject of the portrait?

257

READING BACKWARDS

Read these backwards and try to make similar sentences :

Madam I'm Adam.

Able was I ere I saw Elba.

Egad a base tone denotes a bad age.

Roma ibi tibi sedes ibi tibi amor.

258

AVERAGE SPEED

A man makes a trip by motor car at an average speed for the outward journey of 30 miles per hour and returns at an average speed of 20 miles per hour. What is his average speed for the whole journey ?

259

PUZZLE RHYME

Off to the links is all the cry,
For golf is man * * * * * * * *
Be not * * * * * * * * nor slow
* * * * * * * * hit the ball will go.

The puzzle is to fill in the three words, using the same eight letters in each word.

260

Here is a similar one :

When Euclid evolved the * * * * * * * *
Isoceles, scalene and what not
He felt he had done with the tangle
And staggered to bed with a hot tot.

But others with genius unfaltering
Found * * * * * * * * a noun of such worth
Making * * * * * * * * first and then * * * * * * * *
And * * * * * * * * three words at a breath.

261

BLIND BEGGAR

Here is one which is so obvious that it baffles even the most intelligent.

The blind beggar had a brother who died.

The man who died had no brother. What relation was the blind beggar to the man who died?

262

DR. WHEWELL'S PUZZLE SENTENCE

You o a o but I o thee
o o no o but o o me
Then will your o no o be
But give o o I o thee.

263

PUZZLE PUNCTUATION

(1) He said that that that that that woman said ought to have been which.

(2) It was and I said not but.

(3) Time flies you cannot they pass by at such irregular intervals.

(4) I want more space between pig and and and and and whistle.

(5) That that is is that that is not is not is not that it it is.

(6) The murderer spoke fluently half an hour after he was beheaded.

(7) Captain BBBB sent his CCCC to dig pot OOOOOOOO.

(8) Esau Wood saw a saw saw wood as no other wood saw Wood saw would saw wood. Of all the wood saws Wood ever saw saw wood Wood never saw a wood saw that would saw wood as the wood saw Wood saw saw wood would saw wood and I never saw a wood saw that would saw wood as the wood saw Wood saw would saw until I saw Wood saw wood with the wood saw Esau Wood saw saw wood.

264

QUICK CALCULATION

Ask someone to write down a row of figures.

Say he writes 2 3 6 1 4

Then ask a second person to write down a row of figures.

Say 1 3 1 1 5

Then you write down a row, subtracting the last from

99999 = 8 6 8 8 4

Ask a third person to add a row, say 1 6 5 8 2

Then you write down a row again, subtracting the last

from 99999 = 8 3 4 1 7

Then a fourth person adds a row, say 1 2 3 4 5

Then you write your third row, subtracting the last from

99999 = 8 7 6 5 4

Add all the rows together = 3 2 3 6 1 1

You may write down the answer as soon as the first row has been written down. The total may always be found by taking the first number less 3 = 23611 and placing a 3 in front, making 323611.

265

Here are some very old ones which have stood the test of time.

(1) If the B empty put :
    If the B. putting :
(2) Stand take to taking.
      I you throw my

Here is a puzzle for the Post Office.

(3)   Wood
         John
         Hants.

266

How many different squares are there in this figure *and how many different triangles?*

267

THE HIKER

When a hiker came to a cross-roads he found that the signpost had fallen to the ground. How did he find which was the correct road to take to continue his journey?

268

BUYING CIGARS

A man goes into a shop and buys 50 cigars for 50 shillings. They obviously cost one shilling each. He then goes into a second shop and buys 100 cigars for 50 shillings. This lot therefore cost sixpence each. He goes into a third shop and buys 75 cigars for 50 shillings.* How much do they cost each? Is the correct answer ninepence each?

269

THE BOOKSHELF

If 100 books are placed on a bookshelf in the usual way in a row, and each book is 1 inch thick, how far is it from page one of volume one to the last page of volume 100?

270

HERE IS A VERY PERFECT ANAGRAM

Change—Dangers of amateur physicking (*into*)
The sick men pay for drugs again.

---

*There are twelve pence to a shilling.

271

RIDDLE ATTRIBUTED TO LORD MACAULAY

Come let's look at it closely
'Tis a very ugly word
And always makes one shudder
Whenever it is heard.

It mayn't be always wicked,
It must be always bad,
And speaks of sin and sorrow
Enough to make one sad.

If from the twelve letters
You take off the first three
You have the nine remaining
As sad as sad can be.

You seem to make it less,
But in fact you make it more,
For you take in the brute creation
Which was left out before.

Let's see if we can't change it,
I think perchance we might,
Instead of three and nine
Let's make it four and eight.

The change seems very little,
But in truth 'tis very great,
It must be very great,
For only see what's done,
You've changed the ways of sadness
To merriment and fun.

Yes, four and eight, my friends,
Let that be yours and mine
While all the host of demons
Rejoice in three and nine.

272
FIND THE MISSING LETTERS

(1) G D L D P R T F R M P R T F R R T H D X X F
R D D N S

(2) P R S V R Y P R F C T M N V R K P T H S P R C
P T S T N

(3) D N T B R R W F R M T M R R W
D N W R N G S K N W N S R R W
F L S W H N L Y L K F R G L D
C M M N C M F R T S D N T H L D

273
WEIGHING THE SUGAR

A grocer weighs a bag of sugar for a customer on a pair of false scales (unequal arms) on which it registers 45 lbs. The customer puts the bag on the opposite pan of the scales and finds that it now weighs only 20 lbs. What is the correct weight of the bag?

274
ARITHMETICAL PROBLEM

Here is an example of an ancient type of problem. If five times four make thirty-three, what will the fourth of forty be?

275
WEIGHTS PROBLEM

What is the least number of weights which will allow you to weigh every pound from 1 to 40 lb.?

276

MAGIC SQUARE

5	80	59	73	61	3	63	12	13
1	20	55	30	57	28	71	26	81
4	14	31	50	29	60	35	68	78
76	58	46	38	45	40	36	24	6
7	65	33	43	41	39	49	17	75
74	64	48	42	37	44	34	18	8
67	10	47	32	53	22	51	72	15
66	56	27	52	25	54	11	62	16
69	2	23	9	21	79	19	70	77

23	6	19	2	15
4	12	25	8	16
10	18	1	14	22
11	24	7	20	3
17	5	13	21	9

The above magic square of numbers from 1 to 81 is still a complete magic square after each row is removed.

The sum of each whole row = 369
"   "   " row of 7 = 287
"   "   "   "   5 = 205
"   "   "   "   3 = 123

and the central figure 41 is the greatest common divisor of the above sums. The magic square on the right counts 65 in 40 ways.

277

EIGHT DRAUGHTSMEN

Place 8 men on a draught-board so that none will be in line vertically, diagonally or horizontally. The illustration on page 155 shows how this can be done.

278

THE WORKER AND HIS BOSS

A worker who was employed by a tailor asked his boss for an increase in his salary. The tailor replied as follows:

This is a leap year and it has 366 days. You only work 8 hours per day, which is one-third of the 24 hours. Therefore you really work one third of a year, which is equal to 122 days. You do not work on Sundays, so you have 52 days off every year. So 52 from 122 leaves 70 days. You do not work on Saturdays, either, since we are closed, so you lose another 52 days, which, taken from 70, leaves 18 days. You take 4 Bank Holidays every year, which leaves you with 14 days, and since you get a fortnight's holiday every year it seems to me you don't work here at all.

279

THE FARMER AND HIS COWS

A farmer died and left his seventeen cows to his three sons in the following proportion: To the eldest he left half the cows, to his second son one-third, and to the youngest one-ninth. They soon found that it was impossible to divide the legacy to satisfy these conditions. So they went to the local priest, who, after thinking the matter over, solved the problem in this way. He brought his own cow over to the farm, thus making 18 cows in all. He then gave

$$
\begin{array}{llll}
\text{to the eldest} & \tfrac{1}{2} \text{ of the cows} & = 9 \\
\text{,, second} & \tfrac{1}{3} \text{ ,,} & \text{,,} & = 6 \\
\text{,, youngest} & \tfrac{1}{9} \text{ ,,} & \text{,,} & = 2 \\
& & & \overline{} \\
& & & 17 \\
& & & \overline{}
\end{array}
$$

This made up the original 17 cows, so he took his own cow home.

280

THE SANDWICHES

Two hikers sat down at the side of the road to have a meal. The first had five sandwiches and the second three. Just as they were preparing to start a third hiker came along, and as he was without food they agreed to share the eight sandwiches equally. When the meal was finished the third walker said he would pay eightpence* for his share of the meal, but a dispute arose as to the equitable division of the money. The first said that it should be divided in the proportion of 5 to 3. The second said that as all had eaten an equal amount, the money should be divided equally. The third walker said that the first ought to have sevenpence as his share, and that the second walker should only have a penny. Who was correct?

281

THE SNAIL

A snail climbs up a wall which is 20 feet high at the rate of 3 feet each day, but slips back 2 feet every night. How long will it take to get to the top?

282

THE FAMILY

Old Smith had a family of sons and daughters. Each daughter had an equal number of brothers and sisters, but each son had twice as many sisters as brothers. How many boys and girls were there in the family?

*You can substitute cents for pence in this puzzle.

ANSWERS TO THE QUESTIONS IN SECTION NINE

247.—$12\frac{4}{7}$ seconds.—$13\frac{1}{5}$ seconds.

249.—" Cares."

250.—90 minutes.

251.—12111.

252.—The flange of the wheel below the rail.

258.—24 miles per hour.

259.—The words are : IDOLATRY, DILATORY, ADROITLY.

260.—*TRIANGLE*—triangle—*INTEGRAL—ALTERING—RELATING*

262.—   *Translation*

You sigh for a cypher but I sigh for thee
Oh sigh for no cypher but oh sigh for me
Then will your sigh for no cypher be
But give sigh for sigh for I sigh for thee.

265.—   *Translation*

(1) If the grate be empty put coal on.
    If the grate be full, stop putting coal on
(2) I understand you undertake to overthrow my undertaking.

(3)   ⎫   John Underwood,
                     ⎬ =   Andover,
                     ⎭   Hants.

271.—Manslaughter.   Slaughter.   Mans laughter.

272.—(1) add O's.   (2) = E's.   (3) add O's.

273.—$\sqrt{45 \times 20} = 30$ lbs.

274.—$16\frac{1}{2}$.

275.—If the weights may only be placed on one side of the balance the answer is 1—2—4—8—16 and 32 lb. If the weights may be placed in either pan the answer is 1—3—9 and 27 lb.

277.—

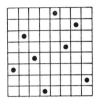

280.—The first walker was entitled to seven times as much money as the second walker.

281.—18 days.

282.—3 sons and 4 daughters.

MISCELLANEOUS

283
BOYS CLIMBING A GARDEN WALL

Bring the left forefinger and the right thumb and the right forefinger and the left thumb together as shown in the illustration. Rotate the right hand (keeping the right forefinger and left thumb together and using them as a pivot), thumb towards you until the thumb is on top and at the same time rotate the left hand in the opposite direction until the forefinger is on top. Bring the right thumb and left forefinger together. Use these latter digits as the pivot, and rotate the left thumb towards you and the right forefinger away from you, thus bringing them on top and in contact.

Continue doing this and at the same time raising both hands until they are on a level with your eyes. Then reverse the motion, lowering the hands. Tell a story of this kind :

Two little boys climbed up, up and up a garden wall to steal some apples which they saw growing on a tree. When they got to the top of the wall (here the hands should be level with your eyes) they looked over the top, but seeing the farmer inside they hurriedly climbed down again (here reverse the motion), got safely to the ground and ran away without being seen.

284
HANDKERCHIEF DOLL

Tie a knot in the middle of one side of a handkerchief and twist the two upper corners to make arms. Hold the handkerchief by the two lower corners and by revolving the hands twist these corners up into legs.

285

FIVE FINGER EXERCISES

(1) BRING the palms of the hands together with the thumbs and fingers of the left hand touching along their length the corresponding fingers of the right hand, but with the second finger of each hand bent down on to the palm and therefore touching each other back to back. It will be easy to separate the thumbs, first and little fingers, but you will have some difficulty in separating the third fingers.

(2) Hold the hands in front of you, palms facing the body, fingers horizontal and close together. Then separate the second and third fingers of the left hand, but keep the first and second and the third and fourth still in contact with each other. Do the same with the right hand. Then reverse the motion, separating the first and second and the third and fourth, but keep the second and third in contact. Then do exercise (1) with the right hand and exercise (2) with the left hand.

(3) Bring the tips of the index fingers close together, palms facing you, fingers horizontal. Rotate the right finger in a vertical circle away from you, and at the same time rotate the left finger towards you. Reverse the motion and see how quickly you can do the exercise.

(4) With the right palm rub your chest with a circular motion and at the same time pat the crown of your head with your left hand.

(5) Put the tips of the fingers of the hands together, palms downwards, fingers horizontal. Ask someone to try to pull your fingers apart by grasping your wrists and pulling in the direction of your fingers.

286

TO LAY OUT AN OVAL FLOWER BED

Fix two pegs in the ground a few feet apart and make a loop from a piece of string about 3 times as long as the distance between the pegs. Place the loop over the pegs and draw the string taut by a marking point. Walk round the pegs, keeping the string taut by the marking point, and draw out on the ground the outline of the oval bed.

287

REVERSING THE MARLINSPIKE

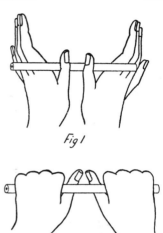

Fig 1

Fig 2

Hold a long pencil between the thumbs as shown in Fig. 1. Turn the hands round and bring the pencil into the position shown in Fig. 2. If this is practised a few times it can be done very easily and smoothly. Then ask someone to try to do it. Although the movement looks absurdly easy, nearly everyone who tries it for the first time will be quite unable to get the pencil into the position shown. It is easier to do the trick in the reverse direction, *i.e.*, to move from Fig. 2 to Fig. 1. Start with the pencil in the position shown in Fig. 2. Then cross the thumbs, putting the thumb of the right hand under the left thumb. Turn the right hand fingers pointing left, thumb downwards and palm facing away from you, and turn the left-hand, thumb upwards and gripping the pencil, fingers pointing right and palm facing towards you. Slip the right thumb under the left end of the pencil, and continue revolving the hands with the palms together until you arrive at Fig. 1. Then reverse the movements, thus going back to Fig. 2.

288

STATIC ELECTRICITY

Lay a sheet of glass on two books so as to leave a space underneath. If the glass is rubbed briskly with a woollen cloth or a silk handkerchief which has been heated in front of the fire, small pieces of paper placed underneath the glass will jump up and down, because the glass has become charged by electricity. Little figures may be cut out of paper, or if small dice are cut out of elder pith they will jump up and then change their spots in a most baffling manner. A stick of sealing wax, if rubbed, will give a rather stronger effect.

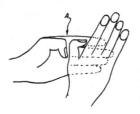

289

BREAKING THE THUMB

Place the hands together, palms horizontal, as shown in the illustration, bending the thumb joints as nearly at right angles as possible, and with the second joint of the left thumb as nearly as possible in a straight line with the first joint of the right thumb. Then bring the first finger of the right hand over to the space A and across at right angles to the first finger of the left hand. The space A will then be covered, and any person looking from the front will think he sees the left thumb only.

Make a slight twisting movement with the right hand and draw it about half an inch to the right. It will look as if you had pulled off the first joint of your left thumb. If neatly done this trick is, for many, a little too realistic.

290

SOAP SOLUTION

To blow bubbles which are sufficiently strong to last some time and to bear handling, it is necessary to have a properly prepared soap solution. Ordinary soap to which glycerine is added is much superior to the usual soap suds, but for the best effect the solution should be made according to the following formula recommended by Professor Boys. Care must be taken to follow the instructions exactly, and to see that only the best materials are used.

To a litre of cold distilled water contained in a clear stoppered bottle add 25 grams of oleate of soda, and let it stand for a day. Then add 300 c.c. of Price's glycerine and well shake. Let the stoppered bottle stand for a week in a dark place. Then by means of a syphon draw off the clear liquid, leaving the scum behind. Add 2 or 3 drops of liquid ammonia, and keep the bottle in a dark place. The liquid must not be warmed or filtered.

BLOWING BUBBLES

The ordinary clay pipe is quite useless for blowing large bubbles, as it is impossible to drive enough air through the small stem. The best tool to use is a piece of tubing about $\frac{1}{4}$ inch in diameter.

Cut a piece of cork about 1 inch in diameter and $\frac{1}{4}$ inch thick. Pierce a hole in the middle of this cork the size of your tube, and fix it on to the extreme end. You now have a large base on the end of the tube and quite large bubbles may be blown without any difficulty. The best and simplest way to study the wonderful colours of the bubbles and the curious angles and planes made by bubbles in contact with each other is to pour a little of the soap solution into a saucer or a plate and, by dipping the end of a small tube into the solution, blow the bubbles up, leaving them in contact with the plate. They can then be studied at leisure.

291

BLOWING A TRIPLE BUBBLE

Pour a small quantity of soap solution into a saucer and set a cork in the centre. On the cork place a penny and on the penny a small cork from a medicine bottle. Place a sixpence on the top of the small cork. Well moisten the corks and coins with soap solution. Put the blow-pipe minus the cork end into the solution in the saucer and blow the large bubble, which will rise over the corks, until it is about 6 or 8 inches in diameter.

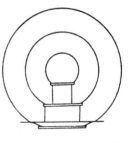

Then dip the point of the pipe in the solution, raise it up and blow the second bubble, letting it rest on the penny. Withdraw the pipe. Dip it into the bottle of solution so as to wet it all the way. Push the end of it through both bubbles and blow the small bubble, letting it rest on the sixpence. By withdrawing some of the air with the pipe from the large bubble it may be made smaller and may be brought down on the inner ones, squeezing them all into a flattened spheroid. A small tube about the size of a straw is useful for manipulating the small inner bubble.

*Or substitute a half dollar for the penny and a quarter for the six-pence.

292

THE OPENING FLOWER

Fold a small square of tinfoil from a cigarette packet diagonally several times, and with a pair of scissors cut out a six or eight-pointed star. Lay this on a cork and set it in the middle of a saucer. Moisten well with soap solution. With the blow-pipe having an enlarged end blow a bubble, and let it rest on the middle of the tinfoil star, which will adhere to and be drawn up by the bubble. You can then enlarge or contract the size of the bubble, thus making the flower open and close at will.

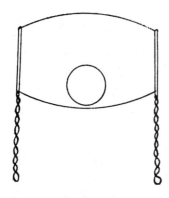

293

THE BUBBLE IN THE BARREL

Make two handled wire rings about 3 inches in diameter. Blow a bubble and let it rest on one of the rings, which should previously be dipped in the soap solution. Bring the second ring down on the bubble parallel to the first one until it adheres to it. Then separate the hands, which will have the effect of drawing the bubble out into a barrel shape. Hold the bubble horizontally and get another person to blow a small bubble inside the larger one by pushing the blowing-tube through the cylindrical surface. Detach the small bubble by tapping the end of the tube. It will fall on the lower surface without sticking to it and may be rolled from one end of the barrel to the other.

294

THE BALLOONIST

Cut out a small figure from paper, and attach it to a short piece of cotton. To the other end of the cotton fix a small disc of paper by passing the cotton through a hole at its centre and fastening by a small knot. Blow a bubble and stick the small disc to its lower surface.

The bubble will float away, carrying the aeronaut with it. If the bubble is blown from a gas pipe it will, of course, rise much better. The best way to do this is to connect the blow-pipe to a gas bracket by means of a small rubber tube. By pinching the tube the flow of gas may be regulated very accurately.

295

BUBBLES ON WIRE FRAME

Make a wire frame in the form of a prism and dip it in the soap solution, when a very beautiful figure will result. Try also a frame in the form of a cube and you will be able to form a wonderful pattern of plane surfaces meeting each other at angles of 120 degrees. Another interesting experiment is to tie a thread of cotton loosely across the diameter of a wire ring. Dip it in soap solution so as to form a film on the ring. The thread will float about anywhere on the film. Then with a spill of blotting paper remove the film from one side, when the thread will be drawn taut as the remaining film will at once contract so as to occupy as small an area as possible.

296

FIRE PICTURES

Draw the outline of a horse, elephant or other suitable subject on a sheet of unglazed paper with a saturated solution of saltpetre. Allow it to dry thoroughly and make a mark at the starting point. Note that the outline should be continuous. Touch the starting point with the end of a glowing match, and the fire will follow round the saltpetre drawing.

Paper may be rendered fire-resisting by dipping it in a saturated solution of washing soda.

COMMUNITY SONGS

Here are six old songs which are not often heard. They are best accompanied by a piano and beer or by beer only. If you are required under penalty to sing a song which the majority of the audience have never heard before, you are sure to win if you choose one of these six. You can make up other verses to suit your audience.

297

EVERY ROSE GROWS BONNY IN TIME

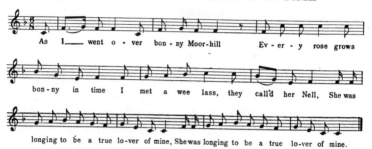

As I____ went o - ver bon - ny Moor-hill Ev - er - y rose grows
bon - ny in time I met a wee lass, they call'd her Nell, She was
longing to be a true lo-ver of mine, She was longing to be a true lo-ver of mine.

It's questions three I'll ask of thee
Every rose grows bonny in time
And questions three you must answer to me
Before I will be a true lover of thine.
Before I will be a true lover of thine.

You must make unto me a cambric shirt,
Every rose grows bonny in time.
Without one stitch of your own needlework,
Before I will be a true lover of thine.
Before I will be a true lover of thine.

You must wash it out in yonder well,
Every rose grows bonny in time,
Where water ne'er wet nor rain ever fell
Before that you be a true lover of mine.
Before that you be a true lover of mine.

You must dry it out on a blackthorn
Every rose grows bonny in time,
Which never budded since Adam was born,
Before I will be a true lover of thine.
Before I will be a true lover of thine.

You must bleach it out on yonder green,
Every rose grows bonny in time,
Where flower ne'er budded nor grass never sprang
Before I will be a true lover of thine.
Before I will be a true lover of thine.

Questions three ye have asked of me,
Every rose grows bonny in time,
And questions three you must answer to me
Or I will not be a true lover of thine.
Or I will not be a true lover of thine.

You must get unto me an acre of land,
Every rose grows bonny in time,
Betwixt the salt sea and the sea sand,
Before I will be a true lover of thine.
Before I will be a true lover of thine.

You must plow it all over with Adam's horn
Every rose grows bonny in time,
And sow it all over with one pickle of corn,
Before you can be a true lover of mine.
Before you can be a true lover of mine.

You must reap it with one peacock's feather,
Every rose grows bonny in time,
Then bind it up with the sting of a nether,
Before you may be a true lover of mine.
Before you may be a true lover of mine.

And when you have done and finished your work
Every rose grows bonny in time,
You may call unto me for your cambric shirt,
And then I will be a true lover of thine.
And then I will be a true lover of thine.

298

PADDY MURPHY

Oh I don't care a mick-ey for O' Ha - ra Nor yet

Mur - phy not to men-tion Mac-na-ma - ra Nor the Sul - tan of the

Turks Nor the I - rish Board o' Works, For they're spoil-in' all the drink in Con-ne-ma - ra.

Says the Sul - tan to the Czar of all the Roo - shias

Nev - er mind a - bout the Imp - eror of the Proo - shias

Pad - dy Mur phy he's a tarror it's a fact re - plied the

Czar He's a bould bad man from the town of Mul - lin - gar.

299

PATSY McGILLIGANS DAUGHTER

I'm a de-cent I-rish man I've a daughter Ma-ry Ann And she

dress-es in the ve-ry best of style— She can speak both Dutch and

Lat-in And she wears both silk and sat-in So the neighbours come a-round for many a mile—

CHORUS

She's a dar-lin' she's a dai-sy And her man-ner's free and

ai-sy She's a mus-cle on her arm like an-y man

And no mat-ter where she goes Sure ev-e-ry-bo-dy

knows That she's Pat-sy Mc-Gil-li-gan's daugh-ter Ma-ry Ann.—

300

WE BURIED HIS CORPSE

Je - re - mi - ah Jos - kin went to see Pro - fes - sor Bald - win

drop from his pa - ra - chute Jer - ry was a big - ot and thought that he Could do the job as

well. So he went and borrowed an old um - brel - la Climb'd to the scaf - fold (his

father was a labour - er) No - bo - dy was by so the poor lit - tle fel - low Jump'd off and down he

CHORUS

fell. So we drew his club mo - ney this morn - ing To the sex - ton we gave

warn - ing No more he'll climb the scaf - fold For his Sun - day clothes are

raf - fled So we drew his club mo - ney this morn - ing.

Miss Macguire thought that she
Would like to be a tight wire walker,
So she fixed the clothes line up in the air
Out in our backyard.
With the line stretched out from pole to pole,
She started off to do the balancing,
But the old line broke and down she fell,
And was spilt upon the floor.

    Chorus.   So we buried her corpse next morning,
           Without the slightest warning ;
             No more will Miss Macguire
             Perform upon the wire,
             For we buried her caw-orpse next morning.

Now old Bill Rastus thought that he
Would like to go on the waves a rowing,
So he borrowed a basket and a bucket of tar,
And off he set to sea.
But the wind came up with great rapidity,
Sent the craft down to the bo-ot-tom,
And the very next day his ham-bones lay
A mouldering on the shore.

    Chorus.   So we buried his corpse next morning,
           Without the slightest warning ;
           No more he'll go a rowing,
           When the stormy winds are blowing,
           For we buried his corpse next morning.

301

JOHNNIE JOHNNIE

Oh John-nie John-nie but love is bon - nie For a wee wee

while— when— it is new But when it's old love, it doth grow

cold love, And fades a - way like the morn - ing dew.

Oh, Johnnie, Johnnie, you are a nice one,
You are the first love that e'er I had ;
Come, kiss me, Johnnie, before you go.
Come, kiss me, Johnnie, before you go.

My lips to kiss ye ne'er shall have, love,
Nor in my arms ye ne'er shall lie,
Until ye grant that one request, love,
That often times you me denied.

It's ower the moss, love, ye needn'a cross, love
Nor through the mire ye needna ride,
For I ha'e gotten a new sweetheart, love,
And ye may choose your own self a bride.

Had I but known when first I kissed you
Young women's hearts were so ill to win,
I would have locked it all in a chest, love,
And screwed it tight with a silver pin.

302

PADDY KANE

By the big turf - fire— and the hearth stone clane Sure there's
not a na - ter cab - in than— that o Pad - dy Kane.

To the ba - by in the cra - dle you can hear his good wife
say Ar - rah go to sleep al - lan-nah till I wet your dad-dy's tay

303

SOLITAIRE

Solitaire is a very old game which has rather gone out of fashion in
recent years, owing perhaps to the fact that all the games are very
much alike. Here are two solutions.

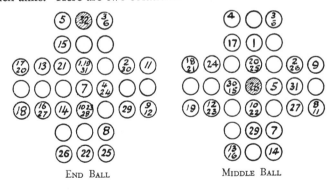

END BALL   MIDDLE BALL

o	x	x
o	x	o
o		x

304

NOUGHTS AND CROSSES

This simple game has been a " keep the children quiet " ruse of harassed mothers since Stonehenge was built. A cross of four lines is made on a sheet of paper. The first player makes a cross in any square he pleases and the second a nought in any other square. The player who first gets three crosses or three noughts in a line is the winner, and has the right to start first the next time. As the starter has the best chance, it is better to let each player start alternately. The game can also be played with sixteen cells instead of nine.

305

TWIRLING THE SERVIETTE RING

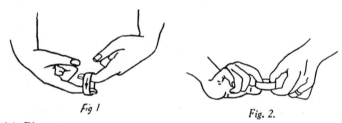

Fig 1.   Fig. 2.

(1) Place a ring between the forefingers and rotate it several times.

(2) Turn the ring quickly into the position shown in Fig. 2.

(3) Bring the tip of the forefinger of the left hand into contact with the tip of the right thumb and the left thumb to touch the right forefinger. This must be done quickly.

(4) Then slowly increase the distance between the thumb and finger of the right hand, but keeping them in contact with those of the left hand. Tilt the hands slightly and the ring will fall to the table. Ask others at the table to try to do the trick. They will all start twirling the rings and very few will be able to get the ring to fall without separating the tips of their fingers.

306

FOX AND GEESE

This simple game is placed on a draught-board.

Four white men are placed on the four white squares at one end of the board and the fox on the middle black square at the other end. The fox can move forwards and backwards one square at a time, but always on the black squares. The geese can only move forward one space at a time and always on the white squares. The game is to hem the fox in so that he cannot move.

307

FOX AND GEESE

The game may also be played on a solitaire board, thus:

There are seventeen geese and they may only move forwards or sideways, one hole at a time. The fox may move forwards, backwards or sideways, but not diagonally. He may take geese by jumping over into a vacant space as in draughts. The game is to hem in the fox so that he cannot move.

308

FLOATING A SEWING NEEDLE IN WATER

Lay a sewing needle (slightly greased) across the forefinger. Gently lower the finger into a bowl of water until the needle touches the surface. Lower the finger still farther, and the needle will be left behind and float quite easily. Then withdraw the finger gently from below the needle. If the needle is magnetised it will point north and south.

309

DIE TRICK

Few are aware that the dots on the opposite faces of a die count seven. Hold a die between the finger and thumb, and show first one side, say the " five." Then show the opposite face, but when turning over the hand to show the number underneath roll the die between the finger and thumb. The result will be that the audience will see the " four " instead of the " two," which is really on the side opposite the " five."

Then hold the die down on the back of your hand with the " five " uppermost and ask someone to guess the number underneath. Anyone who does not know how dice are marked will at once say that the " four " is underneath. If he does, let him lift the die from your hand. If he knows that the " two " is underneath and says so, then turn the die round on a vertical axis, still keeping the " five " uppermost. Lift it up to show the lower side and roll it between the fingers as before. This will change the number again, and you can in this way show that the " one," " three," " four " or " six " is opposite the five.

Another trick of a similar nature is as follows : Hold two dice between the finger and thumb of the right hand so as to show two numbers, say the " four " and the " two." If the corresponding " four " and " two " are covered by the right forefinger, when the dice are rolled between the thumb and forefinger the spots may be made to change their positions, *i.e.*, the number which was nearest to the tip of the forefinger will then be nearest to the root of this finger.

310

CROQUET LAWN

28 yards by 35 yards. There are six hoops and two pegs all spaced 7 yards apart. Two hoops and two pegs are on the centre line. Four hoops are on the cross-lines drawn through the pegs.

311

CUTTING THE MELON

This is the South African method of cutting a melon when serving it up on the dinner-table.

A knife is inserted in the side of the melon and zigzag cuts made all round as shown in the illustration. The halves are then separated, the seeds removed, and other small fruit inserted in their place. The portions are served by continuing the cuts in each half down to the base.

312

THE NINE DRAUGHTSMEN

The game is to remove all the men but one by taking them as in draughts, but diagonal, horizontal or vertical moves are allowed. The last man is to be left in the centre square. The moves are as follows:

With *E* take *H, I, C, A*
  „ *G* „ *D*
  „ *F* „ *B* and *G*
  „ *E* „ *F*

313

CRICKET CREASE

22 yards between stumps. Stumps 8 inches wide by 27 inches high.

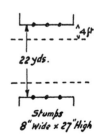

22 yds.

Stumps
8" Wide x 27" High

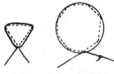

314

THE MYSTERIOUS APPLE

This trick would no doubt puzzle even King George III.

Sew an apple round just under the skin with a needle and thread, letting the needle enter at the exit of each previous stitch. When you get round to the starting point cross the two ends of the cotton and pull on them until the loop comes right out, thus cutting the apple through the centre into two halves. Make another cut at right angles, or several such cuts if you wish. When the fruit is given to a child to peel it will be very astonished to find that the apple has been neatly cut into sections. A banana may be cut into several slices by the same method, three stitches only being required for each cut.

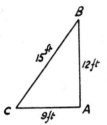

315

LAYING OUT A RIGHT ANGLE

When marking out a tennis court it is necessary to make the corners quite square. To do this put a peg *A* where one of the corners should come, or preferably at the end of the centre line. Then measure along the centre line *A B* a distance of 12 feet and hold the end of the tape line at *B*. Carry the tape round the peg *A*, round a temporary peg at *C* and back to *B*. Hold the 36-foot mark of the tape at *B* and then, stretching the tape by peg *C*, push this peg into the ground, where it coincides with the 21-foot mark on the tape. The angle *B A C* will be a right angle, and the other lines can be built up on this as a base.

316

HOCKEY FIELD

100 yards by 50 yards. Goal 12 feet wide by 7 feet high. Goal line 15 yards from post.

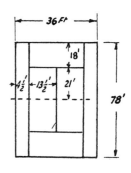

Lawn Tennis

317

LAWN TENNIS COURT

78 feet by 36 feet (see Fig.).

318

FIVES COURT

18 feet by 28 feet.

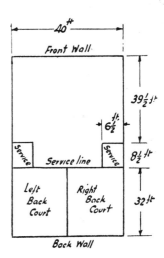

Racquets Court.

319

RACQUETS

320

SQUASH COURT

Length 32 feet. Width 21 feet. Front wall line 15 feet high. Back wall line 7 feet. Short line 18 feet from front wall. Service line 6 feet high. Board 19 inches from ground.

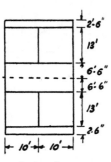

Badminton.

Double Court = 44' × 20'
Single Court = 44' × 17'
Net 5 Ft High at Centre.

321

BADMINTON COURT

Double, 44 feet by 20 feet. Single 44 feet by 17 feet.

322

RUGBY FOOTBALL FIELD

Not to exceed 110 yards by 75 yards. Goal posts must exceed 11 feet high, placed 18 feet 6 inches apart and joined by a cross-bar 10 feet from ground. Marked off with a centre line and 2 lines 25 yards from goal posts.

323

ASSOCIATION FOOTBALL FIELD

Maximum length 130 yards, minimum 100 yards. Maximum breadth 100 yards, minimum 50 yards. Goal posts 8 yards apart and 8 feet high. Penalty area 44 yards by 18 yards. Goal area 20 yards by 6 yards, centre circle 10 yards radius.

324

BASEBALL

Field is a square of 90 feet each side. Pitcher stands 60 feet 6 inches from the home plate. First base is on pitcher's left, second base behind him, third base on his right.

325

LACROSSE

Goals between 100 and 130 yards apart. Goal posts 6 feet high and 6 feet apart. Crease 12 feet square.

326

CURLING RINK

Best length is 44 yards by 15 feet wide. Distance of hogscore is $7\frac{1}{2}$ yards from the tee. Diameter of tie = 14 feet.

327

HEIGHT FINDING

To find the height of a tree or a building by means of a watch. Cut a narrow strip of stiff paper or card half as long again as the diameter of the watch, and bend the two ends at right angles thus ⌐___⌐. Stick the back of the paper to the face of the watch (by wetting it) so that the top edge is exactly in line with 9 minutes past XII and 21 minutes to XII. Then hang the watch on a string by the pendant and hold it up to the level of your eye, with the dial facing to your right. Look along the two top edges of the paper sights and walk backwards until the line of sight joining the two sights coincides with the top of the tree being measured. The height of the tree will be three-quarters of your distance from its base plus the height from your eye to the ground.

328

BOWLING GREEN

About 30 yards square.

329

WATCH COMPASS

To find the points of the compass by means of a watch. Hold the watch horizontally on your palm and orientate it in azimuth until the hour hand points to the sun. The south will be half-way between the hour hand and the figure XII on the dial.

330

COUNTING UP TO FIFTY

This simple game may be played by any number of persons. The first person mentions any number not greater than six. The second person adds to this number any other number not greater than six and so on. The winner is the player who first reaches fifty. If there are two players only, the one who secures the numbers 1—8—15—22—29—36 and 43 is bound to win.

331

CUTTING AN APPLE

1st.—Cut the apple half-way through horizontally.

2nd.—Cut the apple half-way through at right angles to the first cut.

3rd.—Cut horizontally a quarter of the way round so as to join two ends of the 1st and 2nd cuts.

4th.—Cut horizontally quarter of the way round so as to join the other two ends of the 1st and 2nd cuts.

If the apple is peeled first it is rather a puzzle to put the pieces together again.

332
SMUDGEOGRAPHY

By writing or making marks with ink on
a piece of paper along a creased line and
then folding down the paper while the ink
is wet all sorts of amusing figures may be
made. Use plenty of ink ! A variation of
this is to use bright paints. Very beautiful
butterflies can be formed after a little practice. If the pressing is done against a window
pane you can see through the paper and make
any adjustments necessary to bring the butter-
fly to shape.

333
THERMOMETER CONVERSION

To convert Fahrenheit degrees into Centigrade degrees : Deduct
32 from the degrees F., multiply by 5 and divide by 9. Thus :

$$212 \text{ F.} = 212$$
$$- \quad 32$$
$$\overline{180}$$
$$\times \quad 5$$
$$\overline{9) \, 900}$$
$$\overline{100° \text{ C.}}$$

To convert degrees Centigrade into degrees Fahrenheit : Multiply
the degrees C. by 9, divide by 5 and add 32. Thus :

$$100° \text{ C.} = \frac{100 \times 9}{5} + 32 = 212° \text{ F.}$$

334
HOLDING A SWEEPSTAKE ON THE OXFORD AND CAMBRIDGE BOAT RACE

If a sweepstake is arranged on the race in the ordinary way, so soon as the tickets are drawn all those who have received blanks lose any further interest in the result of the sweep. A better method which keeps up the interest of all ticket holders until the race is over is as follows :

When all the subscriptions have been collected the difference between the longest and the shortest time which the race is likely to take is divided up into seconds. For example, the record for the shortest time in which the race has been run is 18 minutes 29 seconds, and the longest race took 26 minutes. The difference between these times is roughly 8 minutes. Divide this into seconds, viz., 480 seconds. If there are, say, 50 tickets in the sweep each ticket is allotted a period of 9 seconds, and the winner is the person who holds a ticket marked with a time embracing that in which the winner actually finishes the race. A second prize may be allotted to the ticket embracing the time taken by the loser. The tickets should be marked thus :—

> 1st ticket all under 18 minutes.
> 2nd ,, 18 minutes to 18 minutes 9 seconds.
> 3rd ,, 18 minutes $9\frac{1}{5}$ seconds to 18 minutes 18 seconds.
> 4th ,, 18 minutes $18\frac{1}{5}$ seconds to 18 minutes 27 seconds.
> last ,, all over 26 minutes.

All the tickets are put into a hat and drawn against the names of the subscribers. Every subscriber thus gets a ticket which has a possible chance. If the race is won in 18 minutes 25 seconds the holder of the 4th ticket is the winner. The subscribers can have quite an amusing time buying and selling shares in their tickets in proportions according to the probability of a win.

Sweepstakes may be held in this manner on the Derby or, in fact, on any event which is accurately timed. Here are a few record times to guide promoters.

Derby, 2 minutes 32$\frac{3}{5}$ seconds.
Kentucky Derby, 2 minutes 1$\frac{4}{5}$ seconds.
Diamond Sculls,   8   „   14   „
Wingfield   „   23   „   12   „
100 yards   9$\frac{2}{5}$ „
120   „   11$\frac{1}{4}$ „
220   „   21$\frac{3}{5}$ „
440   „   47$\frac{2}{5}$ „
880   „   1   „   52$\frac{1}{5}$ „
1 mile   4   „   12$\frac{3}{5}$ „
1 mile walking   6   „   24   „
5   „   „   36   „   0$\frac{1}{5}$ „
10 „   „ 1 hour 15   „   57   „
50 „   „ 7 „   52   „   27   „

If more than one prize is arranged for a race, *e.g.*, for the 1st, 2nd
and 3rd, it will often happen that one ticket will win all three prizes
unless the times on the tickets are more closely spaced round about the
probable time which the race will take.

335

THE MORSE CODE

A	. —	N	— .
B	— . . .	O	— — —
C	— . — .	P	. — — .
D	— . .	Q	— — . —
E	.	R	. — .
F	. . — .	S	. . .
G	— — .	T	—
H	. . . .	U	. . —
I	. .	V	. . . —
J	. — — —	W	. — —
K	— . —	X	— . . —
L	. — . .	Y	— . — —
M	— —	Z	— — . .

336

CHILDREN'S TREASURE HUNT FOR CHRISTMAS PRESENTS

The presents should be distributed in various easily found hiding places in the house, and a direction ticket placed with each parcel telling the children where to look for the next present. A grown-up person should accompany the children to see that they do not go to the places in the wrong order or miss out any of the parcels. In the first place they should be told to look under the door-mat. They will there find a ticket on which is written, "Look under the dining-table." They all troop off to the dining-room, get the present from under the table, open it and find out to whom it belongs. With the parcel is a second card : "Look in the bathroom cupboard." When they have found the parcel there and discovered its owner, they read the ticket which was with it and on which is written, "Boot cupboard," and so on until all the presents have been found. The parcels should be hidden away in the order in which they are to be found. It is best to write out all the tickets beforehand, then all you have to do is to place a card with each present, go to the place indicated on that card and deposit the next parcel and card. This game will keep children amused all Christmas morning.

337

STRETCHER

In the case of an accident a stretcher may be improvised by buttoning up two coats, turning the sleeves outside in and pushing two poles through the sleeves.

A CATALOGUE OF SELECTED DOVER BOOKS
IN ALL FIELDS OF INTEREST

A CATALOGUE OF SELECTED DOVER BOOKS
IN ALL FIELDS OF INTEREST

WHAT IS SCIENCE?, *N. Campbell*
The role of experiment and measurement, the function of mathematics, the nature of scientific laws, the difference between laws and theories, the limitations of science, and many similarly provocative topics are treated clearly and without technicalities by an eminent scientist. "Still an excellent introduction to scientific philosophy," H. Margenau in *Physics Today*. "A first-rate primer . . . deserves a wide audience," *Scientific American*. 192pp. 5⅜ x 8.
60043-2 Paperbound $1.25

THE NATURE OF LIGHT AND COLOUR IN THE OPEN AIR, *M. Minnaert*
Why are shadows sometimes blue, sometimes green, or other colors depending on the light and surroundings? What causes mirages? Why do multiple suns and moons appear in the sky? Professor Minnaert explains these unusual phenomena and hundreds of others in simple, easy-to-understand terms based on optical laws and the properties of light and color. No mathematics is required but artists, scientists, students, and everyone fascinated by these "tricks" of nature will find thousands of useful and amazing pieces of information. Hundreds of observational experiments are suggested which require no special equipment. 200 illustrations; 42 photos. xvi + 362pp. 5⅜ x 8.
20196-1 Paperbound $2.00

THE STRANGE STORY OF THE QUANTUM, AN ACCOUNT FOR THE GENERAL READER OF THE GROWTH OF IDEAS UNDERLYING OUR PRESENT ATOMIC KNOWLEDGE, *B. Hoffmann*
Presents lucidly and expertly, with barest amount of mathematics, the problems and theories which led to modern quantum physics. Dr. Hoffmann begins with the closing years of the 19th century, when certain trifling discrepancies were noticed, and with illuminating analogies and examples takes you through the brilliant concepts of Planck, Einstein, Pauli, Broglie, Bohr, Schroedinger, Heisenberg, Dirac, Sommerfeld, Feynman, etc. This edition includes a new, long postscript carrying the story through 1958. "Of the books attempting an account of the history and contents of our modern atomic physics which have come to my attention, this is the best," H. Margenau, Yale University, in *American Journal of Physics*. 32 tables and line illustrations. Index. 275pp. 5⅜ x 8.
20518-5 Paperbound $2.00

GREAT IDEAS OF MODERN MATHEMATICS: THEIR NATURE AND USE, *Jagjit Singh*
Reader with only high school math will understand main mathematical ideas of modern physics, astronomy, genetics, psychology, evolution, etc. better than many who use them as tools, but comprehend little of their basic structure. Author uses his wide knowledge of non-mathematical fields in brilliant exposition of differential equations, matrices, group theory, logic, statistics, problems of mathematical foundations, imaginary numbers, vectors, etc. Original publication. 2 appendixes. 2 indexes. 65 ills. 322pp. 5⅜ x 8.
20587-8 Paperbound $2.25

THE MUSIC OF THE SPHERES: THE MATERIAL UNIVERSE — FROM ATOM TO QUASAR, SIMPLY EXPLAINED, *Guy Murchie*
Vast compendium of fact, modern concept and theory, observed and calculated data, historical background guides intelligent layman through the material universe. Brilliant exposition of earth's construction, explanations for moon's craters, atmospheric components of Venus and Mars (with data from recent fly-by's), sun spots, sequences of star birth and death, neighboring galaxies, contributions of Galileo, Tycho Brahe, Kepler, etc.; and (Vol. 2) construction of the atom (describing newly discovered sigma and xi subatomic particles), theories of sound, color and light, space and time, including relativity theory, quantum theory, wave theory, probability theory, work of Newton, Maxwell, Faraday, Einstein, de Broglie, etc. "Best presentation yet offered to the intelligent general reader," *Saturday Review*. Revised (1967). Index. 319 illustrations by the author. Total of xx + 644pp. 5⅜ x 8½.
21809-0, 21810-4   Two volume set, paperbound $5.00

FOUR LECTURES ON RELATIVITY AND SPACE, *Charles Proteus Steinmetz*
Lecture series, given by great mathematician and electrical engineer, generally considered one of the best popular-level expositions of special and general relativity theories and related questions. Steinmetz translates complex mathematical reasoning into language accessible to laymen through analogy, example and comparison. Among topics covered are relativity of motion, location, time; of mass; acceleration; 4-dimensional time-space; geometry of the gravitational field; curvature and bending of space; non-Euclidean geometry. Index. 40 illustrations. x + 142pp. 5⅜ x 8½.   61771-8 Paperbound $1.35

HOW TO KNOW THE WILD FLOWERS, *Mrs. William Starr Dana*
Classic nature book that has introduced thousands to wonders of American wild flowers. Color-season principle of organization is easy to use, even by those with no botanical training, and the genial, refreshing discussions of history, folklore, uses of over 1,000 native and escape flowers, foliage plants are informative as well as fun to read. Over 170 full-page plates, collected from several editions, may be colored in to make permanent records of finds. Revised to conform with 1950 edition of Gray's Manual of Botany. xlii + 438pp. 5⅜ x 8½.   20332-8 Paperbound $2.50

MANUAL OF THE TREES OF NORTH AMERICA, *Charles Sprague Sargent*
Still unsurpassed as most comprehensive, reliable study of North American tree characteristics, precise locations and distribution. By dean of American dendrologists. Every tree native to U.S., Canada, Alaska; 185 genera, 717 species, described in detail—leaves, flowers, fruit, winterbuds, bark, wood, growth habits, etc. plus discussion of varieties and local variants, immaturity variations. Over 100 keys, including unusual 11-page analytical key to genera, aid in identification. 783 clear illustrations of flowers, fruit, leaves. An unmatched permanent reference work for all nature lovers. Second enlarged (1926) edition. Synopsis of families. Analytical key to genera. Glossary of technical terms. Index. 783 illustrations, 1 map. Total of 982pp. 5⅜ x 8.
20277-1, 20278-X Two volume set, paperbound $6.00

IT'S FUN TO MAKE THINGS FROM SCRAP MATERIALS,
Evelyn Glantz Hershoff
What use are empty spools, tin cans, bottle tops? What can be made from
rubber bands, clothes pins, paper clips, and buttons? This book provides
simply worded instructions and large diagrams showing you how to make
cookie cutters, toy trucks, paper turkeys, Halloween masks, telephone sets,
aprons, linoleum block- and spatter prints — in all 399 projects! Many are easy
enough for young children to figure out for themselves; some challenging
enough to entertain adults; all are remarkably ingenious ways to make things
from materials that cost pennies or less! Formerly "Scrap Fun for Everyone."
Index. 214 illustrations. 373pp. 5⅜ x 8½.   21251-3 Paperbound $1.75

SYMBOLIC LOGIC and THE GAME OF LOGIC, *Lewis Carroll*
"Symbolic Logic" is not concerned with modern symbolic logic, but is instead
a collection of over 380 problems posed with charm and imagination, using
the syllogism and a fascinating diagrammatic method of drawing conclusions.
In "The Game of Logic" Carroll's whimsical imagination devises a logical game
played with 2 diagrams and counters (included) to manipulate hundreds of
tricky syllogisms. The final section, "Hit or Miss" is a lagniappe of 101 additional puzzles in the delightful Carroll manner. Until this reprint edition,
both of these books were rarities costing up to $15 each. Symbolic Logic:
Index. xxxi + 199pp. The Game of Logic: 96pp. 2 vols. bound as one. 5⅜ x 8.
20492-8 Paperbound $2.50

MATHEMATICAL PUZZLES OF SAM LOYD, PART I
selected and edited by M. Gardner
Choice puzzles by the greatest American puzzle creator and innovator. Selected
from his famous collection, "Cyclopedia of Puzzles," they retain the unique
style and historical flavor of the originals. There are posers based on arithmetic,
algebra, probability, game theory, route tracing, topology, counter and sliding
block, operations research, geometrical dissection. Includes the famous "14-15"
puzzle which was a national craze, and his "Horse of a Different Color" which
sold millions of copies. 117 of his most ingenious puzzles in all. 120 line
drawings and diagrams. Solutions. Selected references. xx + 167pp. 5⅜ x 8.
20498-7 Paperbound $1.35

STRING FIGURES AND HOW TO MAKE THEM, *Caroline Furness Jayne*
107 string figures plus variations selected from the best primitive and modern
examples developed by Navajo, Apache, pygmies of Africa, Eskimo, in Europe,
Australia, China, etc. The most readily understandable, easy-to-follow book in
English on perennially popular recreation. Crystal-clear exposition; step-by-
step diagrams. Everyone from kindergarten children to adults looking for
unusual diversion will be endlessly amused. Index. Bibliography. Introduction
by A. C. Haddon. 17 full-page plates, 960 illustrations. xxiii + 401pp. 5⅜ x 8½.
20152-X Paperbound $2.25

PAPER FOLDING FOR BEGINNERS, *W. D. Murray and F. J. Rigney*
A delightful introduction to the varied and entertaining Japanese art of
origami (paper folding), with a full, crystal-clear text that anticipates every
difficulty; over 275 clearly labeled diagrams of all important stages in creation.
You get results at each stage, since complex figures are logically developed
from simpler ones. 43 different pieces are explained: sailboats, frogs, roosters,
etc. 6 photographic plates. 279 diagrams. 95pp. 5⅜ x 8⅜.
20713-7 Paperbound $1.00

PRINCIPLES OF ART HISTORY,
H. Wölfflin
Analyzing such terms as "baroque," "classic," "neoclassic," "primitive," "picturesque," and 164 different works by artists like Botticelli, van Cleve, Dürer, Hobbema, Holbein, Hals, Rembrandt, Titian, Brueghel, Vermeer, and many others, the author establishes the classifications of art history and style on a firm, concrete basis. This classic of art criticism shows what really occurred between the 14th-century primitives and the sophistication of the 18th century in terms of basic attitudes and philosophies. "A remarkable lesson in the art of seeing," *Sat. Rev. of Literature.* Translated from the 7th German edition. 150 illustrations. 254pp. 6⅛ x 9¼. 20276-3 Paperbound $2.25

PRIMITIVE ART,
Franz Boas
This authoritative and exhaustive work by a great American anthropologist covers the entire gamut of primitive art. Pottery, leatherwork, metal work, stone work, wood, basketry, are treated in detail. Theories of primitive art, historical depth in art history, technical virtuosity, unconscious levels of patterning, symbolism, styles, literature, music, dance, etc. A must book for the interested layman, the anthropologist, artist, handicrafter (hundreds of unusual motifs), and the historian. Over 900 illustrations (50 ceramic vessels, 12 totem poles, etc.). 376pp. 5⅜ x 8. 20025-6 Paperbound $2.50

THE GENTLEMAN AND CABINET MAKER'S DIRECTOR,
Thomas Chippendale
A reprint of the 1762 catalogue of furniture designs that went on to influence generations of English and Colonial and Early Republic American furniture makers. The 200 plates, most of them full-page sized, show Chippendale's designs for French (Louis XV), Gothic, and Chinese-manner chairs, sofas, canopy and dome beds, cornices, chamber organs, cabinets, shaving tables, commodes, picture frames, frets, candle stands, chimney pieces, decorations, etc. The drawings are all elegant and highly detailed; many include construction diagrams and elevations. A supplement of 24 photographs shows surviving pieces of original and Chippendale-style pieces of furniture. Brief biography of Chippendale by N. I. Bienenstock, editor of *Furniture World.* Reproduced from the 1762 edition. 200 plates, plus 19 photographic plates. vi + 249pp. 9⅛ x 12¼. 21601-2 Paperbound $3.50

AMERICAN ANTIQUE FURNITURE: A BOOK FOR AMATEURS,
Edgar G. Miller, Jr.
Standard introduction and practical guide to identification of valuable American antique furniture. 2115 illustrations, mostly photographs taken by the author in 148 private homes, are arranged in chronological order in extensive chapters on chairs, sofas, chests, desks, bedsteads, mirrors, tables, clocks, and other articles. Focus is on furniture accessible to the collector, including simpler pieces and a larger than usual coverage of Empire style. Introductory chapters identify structural elements, characteristics of various styles, how to avoid fakes, etc. "We are frequently asked to name some book on American furniture that will meet the requirements of the novice collector, the beginning dealer, and . . . the general public. . . . We believe Mr. Miller's two volumes more completely satisfy this specification than any other work," *Antiques.* Appendix. Index. Total of vi + 1106pp. 7⅞ x 10¾. 21599-7, 21600-4 Two volume set, paperbound $7.50

THE BAD CHILD'S BOOK OF BEASTS, MORE BEASTS FOR WORSE CHILDREN, and A MORAL ALPHABET, *H. Belloc*
Hardly and anthology of humorous verse has appeared in the last 50 years without at least a couple of these famous nonsense verses. But one must see the entire volumes — with all the delightful original illustrations by Sir Basil Blackwood — to appreciate fully Belloc's charming and witty verses that play so subacidly on the platitudes of life and morals that beset his day — and ours. A great humor classic. Three books in one. Total of 157pp. 5⅜ x 8.
20749-8 Paperbound $1.00

THE DEVIL'S DICTIONARY, *Ambrose Bierce*
Sardonic and irreverent barbs puncturing the pomposities and absurdities of American politics, business, religion, literature, and arts, by the country's greatest satirist in the classic tradition. Epigrammatic as Shaw, piercing as Swift, American as Mark Twain, Will Rogers, and Fred Allen, Bierce will always remain the favorite of a small coterie of enthusiasts, and of writers and speakers whom he supplies with "some of the most gorgeous witticisms of the English language" (H. L. Mencken). Over 1000 entries in alphabetical order. 144pp. 5⅜ x 8.
20487-1 Paperbound $1.00

THE COMPLETE NONSENSE OF EDWARD LEAR.
This is the only complete edition of this master of gentle madness available at a popular price. *A Book of Nonsense, Nonsense Songs, More Nonsense Songs and Stories* in their entirety with all the old favorites that have delighted children and adults for years. The Dong With A Luminous Nose, The Jumblies, The Owl and the Pussycat, and hundreds of other bits of wonderful nonsense. 214 limericks, 3 sets of Nonsense Botany, 5 Nonsense Alphabets, 546 drawings by Lear himself, and much more. 320pp. 5⅜ x 8. 20167-8 Paperbound $1.75

THE WIT AND HUMOR OF OSCAR WILDE, *ed. by Alvin Redman*
Wilde at his most brilliant, in 1000 epigrams exposing weaknesses and hypocrisies of "civilized" society. Divided into 49 categories—sin, wealth, women, America, etc.—to aid writers, speakers. Includes excerpts from his trials, books, plays, criticism. Formerly "The Epigrams of Oscar Wilde." Introduction by Vyvyan Holland, Wilde's only living son. Introductory essay by editor. 260pp. 5⅜ x 8.
20602-5 Paperbound $1.50

A CHILD'S PRIMER OF NATURAL HISTORY, *Oliver Herford*
Scarcely an anthology of whimsy and humor has appeared in the last 50 years without a contribution from Oliver Herford. Yet the works from which these examples are drawn have been almost impossible to obtain! Here at last are Herford's improbable definitions of a menagerie of familiar and weird animals, each verse illustrated by the author's own drawings. 24 drawings in 2 colors; 24 additional drawings. vii + 95pp. 6½ x 6. 21647-0 Paperbound $1.00

THE BROWNIES: THEIR BOOK, *Palmer Cox*
The book that made the Brownies a household word. Generations of readers have enjoyed the antics, predicaments and adventures of these jovial sprites, who emerge from the forest at night to play or to come to the aid of a deserving human. Delightful illustrations by the author decorate nearly every page. 24 short verse tales with 266 illustrations. 155pp. 6⅝ x 9¼.
21265-3 Paperbound $1.50

THE PRINCIPLES OF PSYCHOLOGY,
William James
The full long-course, unabridged, of one of the great classics of Western literature and science. Wonderfully lucid descriptions of human mental activity, the stream of thought, consciousness, time perception, memory, imagination, emotions, reason, abnormal phenomena, and similar topics. Original contributions are integrated with the work of such men as Berkeley, Binet, Mills, Darwin, Hume, Kant, Royce, Schopenhauer, Spinoza, Locke, Descartes, Galton, Wundt, Lotze, Herbart, Fechner, and scores of others. All contrasting interpretations of mental phenomena are examined in detail—introspective analysis, philosophical interpretation, and experimental research. "A classic," *Journal of Consulting Psychology.* "The main lines are as valid as ever," *Psychoanalytical Quarterly.* "Standard reading . . . a classic of interpretation," *Psychiatric Quarterly.* 94 illustrations. 1408pp. 5⅜ x 8.
20381-6, 20382-4 Two volume set, paperbound $6.00

VISUAL ILLUSIONS: THEIR CAUSES, CHARACTERISTICS AND APPLICATIONS,
M. Luckiesh
"Seeing is deceiving," asserts the author of this introduction to virtually every type of optical illusion known. The text both describes and explains the principles involved in color illusions, figure-ground, distance illusions, etc. 100 photographs, drawings and diagrams prove how easy it is to fool the sense: circles that aren't round, parallel lines that seem to bend, stationary figures that seem to move as you stare at them — illustration after illustration strains our credulity at what we see. Fascinating book from many points of view, from applications for artists, in camouflage, etc. to the psychology of vision. New introduction by William Ittleson, Dept. of Psychology, Queens College. Index. Bibliography. xxi + 252pp. 5⅜ x 8½.
21530-X Paperbound $1.50

FADS AND FALLACIES IN THE NAME OF SCIENCE,
Martin Gardner
This is the standard account of various cults, quack systems, and delusions which have masqueraded as science: hollow earth fanatics, Reich and orgone sex energy, dianetics, Atlantis, multiple moons, Forteanism, flying saucers, medical fallacies like iridiagnosis, zone therapy, etc. A new chapter has been added on Bridey Murphy, psionics, and other recent manifestations in this field. This is a fair, reasoned appraisal of eccentric theory which provides excellent inoculation against cleverly masked nonsense. "Should be read by everyone, scientist and non-scientist alike," R. T. Birge, Prof. Emeritus of Physics, Univ. of California; Former President, American Physical Society. Index. x + 365pp. 5⅜ x 8.
20394-8 Paperbound $2.00

ILLUSIONS AND DELUSIONS OF THE SUPERNATURAL AND THE OCCULT,
D. H. Rawcliffe
Holds up to rational examination hundreds of persistent delusions including crystal gazing, automatic writing, table turning, mediumistic trances, mental healing, stigmata, lycanthropy, live burial, the Indian Rope Trick, spiritualism, dowsing, telepathy, clairvoyance, ghosts, ESP, etc. The author explains and exposes the mental and physical deceptions involved, making this not only an exposé of supernatural phenomena, but a valuable exposition of characteristic types of abnormal psychology. Originally titled "The Psychology of the Occult." 14 illustrations. Index. 551pp. 5⅜ x 8. 20503-7 Paperbound $3.50

FAIRY TALE COLLECTIONS, *edited by Andrew Lang*
Andrew Lang's fairy tale collections make up the richest shelf-full of traditional children's stories anywhere available. Lang supervised the translation of stories from all over the world—familiar European tales collected by Grimm, animal stories from Negro Africa, myths of primitive Australia, stories from Russia, Hungary, Iceland, Japan, and many other countries. Lang's selection of translations are unusually high; many authorities consider that the most familiar tales find their best versions in these volumes. All collections are richly decorated and illustrated by H. J. Ford and other artists.

THE BLUE FAIRY BOOK. 37 stories. 138 illustrations. ix + 390pp. 5⅜ x 8½. 21437-0 Paperbound $1.95

THE GREEN FAIRY BOOK. 42 stories. 100 illustrations. xiii + 366pp. 5⅜ x 8½. 21439-7 Paperbound $1.75

THE BROWN FAIRY BOOK. 32 stories. 50 illustrations, 8 in color. xii + 350pp. 5⅜ x 8½. 21438-9 Paperbound $1.95

THE BEST TALES OF HOFFMANN, *edited by E. F. Bleiler*
10 stories by E. T. A. Hoffmann, one of the greatest of all writers of fantasy. The tales include "The Golden Flower Pot," "Automata," "A New Year's Eve Adventure," "Nutcracker and the King of Mice," "Sand-Man," and others. Vigorous characterizations of highly eccentric personalities, remarkably imaginative situations, and intensely fast pacing has made these tales popular all over the world for 150 years. Editor's introduction. 7 drawings by Hoffmann. xxxiii + 419pp. 5⅜ x 8½. 21793-0 Paperbound $2.25

GHOST AND HORROR STORIES OF AMBROSE BIERCE,
edited by E. F. Bleiler
Morbid, eerie, horrifying tales of possessed poets, shabby aristocrats, revived corpses, and haunted malefactors. Widely acknowledged as the best of their kind between Poe and the moderns, reflecting their author's inner torment and bitter view of life. Includes "Damned Thing," "The Middle Toe of the Right Foot," "The Eyes of the Panther," "Visions of the Night," "Moxon's Master," and over a dozen others. Editor's introduction. xxii + 199pp. 5⅜ x 8½. 20767-6 Paperbound $1.50

THREE GOTHIC NOVELS, *edited by E. F. Bleiler*
Originators of the still popular Gothic novel form, influential in ushering in early 19th-century Romanticism. Horace Walpole's *Castle of Otranto*, William Beckford's *Vathek*, John Polidori's *The Vampyre*, and a *Fragment* by Lord Byron are enjoyable as exciting reading or as documents in the history of English literature. Editor's introduction. xi + 291pp. 5⅜ x 8½. 21232-7 Paperbound $2.00

BEST GHOST STORIES OF LEFANU, *edited by E. F. Bleiler*
Though admired by such critics as V. S. Pritchett, Charles Dickens and Henry James, ghost stories by the Irish novelist Joseph Sheridan LeFanu have never become as widely known as his detective fiction. About half of the 16 stories in this collection have never before been available in America. Collection includes "Carmilla" (perhaps the best vampire story ever written), "The Haunted Baronet," "The Fortunes of Sir Robert Ardagh," and the classic "Green Tea." Editor's introduction. 7 contemporary illustrations. Portrait of LeFanu. xii + 467pp. 5⅜ x 8. 20415-4 Paperbound $2.50

EASY-TO-DO ENTERTAINMENTS AND DIVERSIONS WITH COINS, CARDS, STRING, PAPER AND MATCHES, *R. M. Abraham*

Over 300 tricks, games and puzzles will provide young readers with absorbing fun. Sections on card games; paper-folding; tricks with coins, matches and pieces of string; games for the agile; toy-making from common household objects; mathematical recreations; and 50 miscellaneous pastimes. Anyone in charge of groups of youngsters, including hard-pressed parents, and in need of suggestions on how to keep children sensibly amused and quietly content will find this book indispensable. Clear, simple text, copious number of delightful line drawings and illustrative diagrams. Originally titled "Winter Nights' Entertainments." Introduction by Lord Baden Powell. 329 illustrations. v + 186pp. 5⅜ x 8½. 20921-0 Paperbound $1.00

AN INTRODUCTION TO CHESS MOVES AND TACTICS SIMPLY EXPLAINED, *Leonard Barden*

Beginner's introduction to the royal game. Names, possible moves of the pieces, definitions of essential terms, how games are won, etc. explained in 30-odd pages. With this background you'll be able to sit right down and play. Balance of book teaches strategy — openings, middle game, typical endgame play, and suggestions for improving your game. A sample game is fully analyzed. True middle-level introduction, teaching you all the essentials without oversimplifying or losing you in a maze of detail. 58 figures. 102pp. 5⅜ x 8½. 21210-6 Paperbound $1.25

LASKER'S MANUAL OF CHESS, *Dr. Emanuel Lasker*

Probably the greatest chess player of modern times, Dr. Emanuel Lasker held the world championship 28 years, independent of passing schools or fashions. This unmatched study of the game, chiefly for intermediate to skilled players, analyzes basic methods, combinations, position play, the aesthetics of chess, dozens of different openings, etc., with constant reference to great modern games. Contains a brilliant exposition of Steinitz's important theories. Introduction by Fred Reinfeld. Tables of Lasker's tournament record. 3 indices. 308 diagrams. 1 photograph. xxx + 349pp. 5⅜ x 8.20640-8 Paperbound $2.50

COMBINATIONS: THE HEART OF CHESS, *Irving Chernev*

Step-by-step from simple combinations to complex, this book, by a well-known chess writer, shows you the intricacies of pins, counter-pins, knight forks, and smothered mates. Other chapters show alternate lines of play to those taken in actual championship games; boomerang combinations; classic examples of brilliant combination play by Nimzovich, Rubinstein, Tarrasch, Botvinnik, Alekhine and Capablanca. Index. 356 diagrams. ix + 245pp. 5⅜ x 8½. 21744-2 Paperbound $2.00

HOW TO SOLVE CHESS PROBLEMS, *K. S. Howard*

Full of practical suggestions for the fan or the beginner — who knows only the moves of the chessmen. Contains preliminary section and 58 two-move, 46 three-move, and 8 four-move problems composed by 27 outstanding American problem creators in the last 30 years. Explanation of all terms and exhaustive index. "Just what is wanted for the student," Brian Harley. 112 problems, solutions. vi + 171pp. 5⅜ x 8. 20748-X Paperbound $1.50

SOCIAL THOUGHT FROM LORE TO SCIENCE,
H. E. Barnes and H. Becker
An immense survey of sociological thought and ways of viewing, studying, planning, and reforming society from earliest times to the present. Includes thought on society of preliterate peoples, ancient non-Western cultures, and every great movement in Europe, America, and modern Japan. Analyzes hundreds of great thinkers: Plato, Augustine, Bodin, Vico, Montesquieu, Herder, Comte, Marx, etc. Weighs the contributions of utopians, sophists, fascists and communists; economists, jurists, philosophers, ecclesiastics, and every 19th and 20th century school of scientific sociology, anthropology, and social psychology throughout the world. Combines topical, chronological, and regional approaches, treating the evolution of social thought as a process rather than as a series of mere topics. "Impressive accuracy, competence, and discrimination . . . easily the best single survey," *Nation.* Thoroughly revised, with new material up to 1960. 2 indexes. Over 2200 bibliographical notes. Three volume set. Total of 1586pp. 5⅜ x 8.

20901-6, 20902-4, 20903-2 Three volume set, paperbound $9.00

A HISTORY OF HISTORICAL WRITING, *Harry Elmer Barnes*
Virtually the only adequate survey of the whole course of historical writing in a single volume. Surveys developments from the beginnings of historiography in the ancient Near East and the Classical World, up through the Cold War. Covers major historians in detail, shows interrelationship with cultural background, makes clear individual contributions, evaluates and estimates importance; also enormously rich upon minor authors and thinkers who are usually passed over. Packed with scholarship and learning, clear, easily written. Indispensable to every student of history. Revised and enlarged up to 1961. Index and bibliography. xv + 442pp. 5⅜ x 8½.

20104-X Paperbound $2.75

JOHANN SEBASTIAN BACH, *Philipp Spitta*
The complete and unabridged text of the definitive study of Bach. Written some 70 years ago, it is still unsurpassed for its coverage of nearly all aspects of Bach's life and work. There could hardly be a finer non-technical introduction to Bach's music than the detailed, lucid analyses which Spitta provides for hundreds of individual pieces. 26 solid pages are devoted to the B minor mass, for example, and 30 pages to the glorious St. Matthew Passion. This monumental set also includes a major analysis of the music of the 18th century: Buxtehude, Pachelbel, etc. "Unchallenged as the last word on one of the supreme geniuses of music," John Barkham, *Saturday Review Syndicate.* Total of 1819pp. Heavy cloth binding. 5⅜ x 8.

22278-0, 22279-9 Two volume set, clothbound $15.00

BEETHOVEN AND HIS NINE SYMPHONIES, *George Grove*
In this modern middle-level classic of musicology Grove not only analyzes all nine of Beethoven's symphonies very thoroughly in terms of their musical structure, but also discusses the circumstances under which they were written, Beethoven's stylistic development, and much other background material. This is an extremely rich book, yet very easily followed; it is highly recommended to anyone seriously interested in music. Over 250 musical passages. Index. viii + 407pp. 5⅜ x 8.

20334-4 Paperbound $2.25

THREE SCIENCE FICTION NOVELS,
John Taine
Acknowledged by many as the best SF writer of the 1920's, Taine (under the name Eric Temple Bell) was also a Professor of Mathematics of considerable renown. Reprinted here are *The Time Stream*, generally considered Taine's best, *The Greatest Game*, a biological-fiction novel, and *The Purple Sapphire*, involving a supercivilization of the past. Taine's stories tie fantastic narratives to frameworks of original and logical scientific concepts. Speculation is often profound on such questions as the nature of time, concept of entropy, cyclical universes, etc. 4 contemporary illustrations. v + 532pp. 5⅜ x 8⅜.

21180-0 Paperbound $2.50

SEVEN SCIENCE FICTION NOVELS,
H. G. Wells
Full unabridged texts of 7 science-fiction novels of the master. Ranging from biology, physics, chemistry, astronomy, to sociology and other studies, Mr. Wells extrapolates whole worlds of strange and intriguing character. "One will have to go far to match this for entertainment, excitement, and sheer pleasure . . ."*New York Times*. Contents: The Time Machine, The Island of Dr. Moreau, The First Men in the Moon, The Invisible Man, The War of the Worlds, The Food of the Gods, In The Days of the Comet. 1015pp. 5⅜ x 8.

20264-X Clothbound $5.00

28 SCIENCE FICTION STORIES OF H. G. WELLS.
Two full, unabridged novels, *Men Like Gods* and *Star Begotten,* plus 26 short stories by the master science-fiction writer of all time! Stories of space, time, invention, exploration, futuristic adventure. Partial contents: *The Country of the Blind, In the Abyss, The Crystal Egg, The Man Who Could Work Miracles, A Story of Days to Come, The Empire of the Ants, The Magic Shop, The Valley of the Spiders, A Story of the Stone Age, Under the Knife, Sea Raiders,* etc. An indispensable collection for the library of anyone interested in science fiction adventure. 928pp. 5⅜ x 8.

20265-8 Clothbound $5.00

THREE MARTIAN NOVELS,
Edgar Rice Burroughs
Complete, unabridged reprinting, in one volume, of Thuvia, Maid of Mars; Chessmen of Mars; The Master Mind of Mars. Hours of science-fiction adventure by a modern master storyteller. Reset in large clear type for easy reading. 16 illustrations by J. Allen St. John. vi + 490pp. 5⅜ x 8½.

20039-6 Paperbound $2.50

AN INTELLECTUAL AND CULTURAL HISTORY OF THE WESTERN WORLD,
Harry Elmer Barnes
Monumental 3-volume survey of intellectual development of Europe from primitive cultures to the present day. Every significant product of human intellect traced through history: art, literature, mathematics, physical sciences, medicine, music, technology, social sciences, religions, jurisprudence, education, etc. Presentation is lucid and specific, analyzing in detail specific discoveries, theories, literary works, and so on. Revised (1965) by recognized scholars in specialized fields under the direction of Prof. Barnes. Revised bibliography. Indexes. 24 illustrations. Total of xxix + 1318pp.

21275-0, 21276-9, 21277-7 Three volume set, paperbound $8.25

HEAR ME TALKIN' TO YA, *edited by Nat Shapiro and Nat Hentoff*
In their own words, Louis Armstrong, King Oliver, Fletcher Henderson, Bunk
Johnson, Bix Beiderbecke, Billy Holiday, Fats Waller, Jelly Roll Morton,
Duke Ellington, and many others comment on the origins of jazz in New
Orleans and its growth in Chicago's South Side, Kansas City's jam sessions,
Depression Harlem, and the modernism of the West Coast schools. Taken
from taped conversations, letters, magazine articles, other first-hand sources.
Editors' introduction. xvi + 429pp. 5⅜ x 8½.   21726-4 Paperbound $2.00

THE JOURNAL OF HENRY D. THOREAU
A 25-year record by the great American observer and critic, as complete a
record of a great man's inner life as is anywhere available. Thoreau's Journals
served him as raw material for his formal pieces, as a place where he could
develop his ideas, as an outlet for his interests in wild life and plants, in
writing as an art, in classics of literature, Walt Whitman and other contemporaries, in politics, slavery, individual's relation to the State, etc. The
Journals present a portrait of a remarkable man, and are an observant social
history. Unabridged republication of 1906 edition, Bradford Torrey and
Francis H. Allen, editors. Illustrations. Total of 1888pp. 8⅜ x 12¼.
              20312-3, 20313-1 Two volume set, clothbound $30.00

A SHAKESPEARIAN GRAMMAR, *E. A. Abbott*
Basic reference to Shakespeare and his contemporaries, explaining through
thousands of quotations from Shakespeare, Jonson, Beaumont and Fletcher,
North's *Plutarch* and other sources the grammatical usage differing from the
modern. First published in 1870 and written by a scholar who spent much of
his life isolating principles of Elizabethan language, the book is unlikely ever
to be superseded. Indexes. xxiv + 511pp. 5⅜ x 8½. 21582-2 Paperbound $3.00

FOLK-LORE OF SHAKESPEARE, *T. F. Thistelton Dyer*
Classic study, drawing from Shakespeare a large body of references to supernatural beliefs, terminology of falconry and hunting, games and sports, good
luck charms, marriage customs, folk medicines, superstitions about plants,
animals, birds, argot of the underworld, sexual slang of London, proverbs,
drinking customs, weather lore, and much else. From full compilation comes
a mirror of the 17th-century popular mind. Index. ix + 526pp. 5⅜ x 8½.
                                      21614-4 Paperbound $2.75

THE NEW VARIORUM SHAKESPEARE, *edited by H. H. Furness*
By far the richest editions of the plays ever produced in any country or
language. Each volume contains complete text (usually First Folio) of the
play, all variants in Quarto and other Folio texts, editorial changes by every
major editor to Furness's own time (1900), footnotes to obscure references or
language, extensive quotes from literature of Shakespearian criticism, essays
on plot sources (often reprinting sources in full), and much more.

HAMLET, *edited by H. H. Furness*
Total of xxvi + 905pp. 5⅜ x 8½.
                    21004-9, 21005-7 Two volume set, paperbound $5.25

TWELFTH NIGHT, *edited by H. H. Furness*
Index. xxii + 434pp. 5⅜ x 8½.   21189-4 Paperbound $2.75

LA BOHEME BY GIACOMO PUCCINI,
translated and introduced by Ellen H. Bleiler
Complete handbook for the operagoer, with everything needed for full enjoyment except the musical score itself. Complete Italian libretto, with new, modern English line-by-line translation—the only libretto printing all repeats; biography of Puccini; the librettists; background to the opera, Murger's La Boheme, etc.; circumstances of composition and performances; plot summary; and pictorial section of 73 illustrations showing Puccini, famous singers and performances, etc. Large clear type for easy reading. 124pp. 5⅜ x 8½.
20404-9 Paperbound $1.25

ANTONIO STRADIVARI: HIS LIFE AND WORK (1644-1737),
W. Henry Hill, Arthur F. Hill, and Alfred E. Hill
Still the only book that really delves into life and art of the incomparable Italian craftsman, maker of the finest musical instruments in the world today. The authors, expert violin-makers themselves, discuss Stradivari's ancestry, his construction and finishing techniques, distinguished characteristics of many of his instruments and their locations. Included, too, is story of introduction of his instruments into France, England, first revelation of their supreme merit, and information on his labels, number of instruments made, prices, mystery of ingredients of his varnish, tone of pre-1684 Stradivari violin and changes between 1684 and 1690. An extremely interesting, informative account for all music lovers, from craftsman to concert-goer. Republication of original (1902) edition. New introduction by Sydney Beck, Head of Rare Book and Manuscript Collections, Music Division, New York Public Library. Analytical index by Rembert Wurlitzer. Appendixes. 68 illustrations. 30 full-page plates. 4 in color. xxvi + 315pp. 5⅜ x 8½.
20425-1 Paperbound $2.25

MUSICAL AUTOGRAPHS FROM MONTEVERDI TO HINDEMITH,
Emanuel Winternitz
For beauty, for intrinsic interest, for perspective on the composer's personality, for subtleties of phrasing, shading, emphasis indicated in the autograph but suppressed in the printed score, the mss. of musical composition are fascinating documents which repay close study in many different ways. This 2-volume work reprints facsimiles of mss. by virtually every major composer, and many minor figures—196 examples in all. A full text points out what can be learned from mss., analyzes each sample. Index. Bibliography. 18 figures. 196 plates. Total of 170pp. of text. 7⅞ x 10¾.
21312-9, 21313-7 Two volume set, paperbound $5.00

J. S. BACH,
Albert Schweitzer
One of the few great full-length studies of Bach's life and work, and the study upon which Schweitzer's renown as a musicologist rests. On first appearance (1911), revolutionized Bach performance. The only writer on Bach to be musicologist, performing musician, and student of history, theology and philosophy, Schweitzer contributes particularly full sections on history of German Protestant church music, theories on motivic pictorial representations in vocal music, and practical suggestions for performance. Translated by Ernest Newman. Indexes. 5 illustrations. 650 musical examples. Total of xix + 928pp. 5⅜ x 8½.
21631-4, 21632-2 Two volume set, paperbound $4.50

THE METHODS OF ETHICS, *Henry Sidgwick*
Propounding no organized system of its own, study subjects every major methodological approach to ethics to rigorous, objective analysis. Study discusses and relates ethical thought of Plato, Aristotle, Bentham, Clarke, Butler, Hobbes, Hume, Mill, Spencer, Kant, and dozens of others. Sidgwick retains conclusions from each system which follow from ethical premises, rejecting the faulty. Considered by many in the field to be among the most important treatises on ethical philosophy. Appendix. Index. xlvii + 528pp. 5⅜ x 8½.
21608-X Paperbound $2.50

TEUTONIC MYTHOLOGY, *Jakob Grimm*
A milestone in Western culture; the work which established on a modern basis the study of history of religions and comparative religions. 4-volume work assembles and interprets everything available on religious and folkloristic beliefs of Germanic people (including Scandinavians, Anglo-Saxons, etc.). Assembling material from such sources as Tacitus, surviving Old Norse and Icelandic texts, archeological remains, folktales, surviving superstitions, comparative traditions, linguistic analysis, etc. Grimm explores pagan deities, heroes, folklore of nature, religious practices, and every other area of pagan German belief. To this day, the unrivaled, definitive, exhaustive study. Translated by J. S. Stallybrass from 4th (1883) German edition. Indexes. Total of lxxvii + 1887pp. 5⅜ x 8½.
21602-0, 21603-9, 21604-7, 21605-5 Four volume set, paperbound $11.00

THE I CHING, *translated by James Legge*
Called "The Book of Changes" in English, this is one of the Five Classics edited by Confucius, basic and central to Chinese thought. Explains perhaps the most complex system of divination known, founded on the theory that all things happening at any one time have characteristic features which can be isolated and related. Significant in Oriental studies, in history of religions and philosophy, and also to Jungian psychoanalysis and other areas of modern European thought. Index. Appendixes. 6 plates. xxi + 448pp. 5⅜ x 8½.
21062-6 Paperbound $2.75

HISTORY OF ANCIENT PHILOSOPHY, *W. Windelband*
One of the clearest, most accurate comprehensive surveys of Greek and Roman philosophy. Discusses ancient philosophy in general, intellectual life in Greece in the 7th and 6th centuries B.C., Thales, Anaximander, Anaximenes, Heraclitus, the Eleatics, Empedocles, Anaxagoras, Leucippus, the Pythagoreans, the Sophists, Socrates, Democritus (20 pages), Plato (50 pages), Aristotle (70 pages), the Peripatetics, Stoics, Epicureans, Sceptics, Neo-platonists, Christian Apologists, etc. 2nd German edition translated by H. E. Cushman. xv + 393pp. 5⅜ x 8.
20357-3 Paperbound $2.25

THE PALACE OF PLEASURE, *William Painter*
Elizabethan versions of Italian and French novels from *The Decameron*, Cinthio, Straparola, Queen Margaret of Navarre, and other continental sources — the very work that provided Shakespeare and dozens of his contemporaries with many of their plots and sub-plots and, therefore, justly considered one of the most influential books in all English literature. It is also a book that any reader will still enjoy. Total of cviii + 1,224pp.
21691-8, 21692-6, 21693-4 Three volume set, paperbound $6.75

THE WONDERFUL WIZARD OF OZ, *L. F. Baum*
All the original W. W. Denslow illustrations in full color—as much a part of "The Wizard" as Tenniel's drawings are of "Alice in Wonderland." "The Wizard" is still America's best-loved fairy tale, in which, as the author expresses it, "The wonderment and joy are retained and the heartaches and nightmares left out." Now today's young readers can enjoy every word and wonderful picture of the original book. New introduction by Martin Gardner. A Baum bibliography. 23 full-page color plates. viii + 268pp. 5⅜ x 8.
20691-2 Paperbound $1.95

THE MARVELOUS LAND OF OZ, *L. F. Baum*
This is the equally enchanting sequel to the "Wizard," continuing the adventures of the Scarecrow and the Tin Woodman. The hero this time is a little boy named Tip, and all the delightful Oz magic is still present. This is the Oz book with the Animated Saw-Horse, the Woggle-Bug, and Jack Pumpkinhead. All the original John R. Neill illustrations, 10 in full color. 287pp. 5⅜ x 8.
20692-0 Paperbound $1.75

ALICE'S ADVENTURES UNDER GROUND, *Lewis Carroll*
The original *Alice in Wonderland*, hand-lettered and illustrated by Carroll himself, and originally presented as a Christmas gift to a child-friend. Adults as well as children will enjoy this charming volume, reproduced faithfully in this Dover edition. While the story is essentially the same, there are slight changes, and Carroll's spritely drawings present an intriguing alternative to the famous Tenniel illustrations. One of the most popular books in Dover's catalogue. Introduction by Martin Gardner. 38 illustrations. 128pp. 5⅜ x 8½.
21482-6 Paperbound $1.00

THE NURSERY "ALICE," *Lewis Carroll*
While most of us consider *Alice in Wonderland* a story for children of all ages, Carroll himself felt it was beyond younger children. He therefore provided this simplified version, illustrated with the famous Tenniel drawings enlarged and colored in delicate tints, for children aged "from Nought to Five." Dover's edition of this now rare classic is a faithful copy of the 1889 printing, including 20 illustrations by Tenniel, and front and back covers reproduced in full color. Introduction by Martin Gardner. xxiii + 67pp. 6⅛ x 9¼.
21610-1 Paperbound $1.75

THE STORY OF KING ARTHUR AND HIS KNIGHTS, *Howard Pyle*
A fast-paced, exciting retelling of the best known Arthurian legends for young readers by one of America's best story tellers and illustrators. The sword Excalibur, wooing of Guinevere, Merlin and his downfall, adventures of Sir Pellias and Gawaine, and others. The pen and ink illustrations are vividly imagined and wonderfully drawn. 41 illustrations. xviii + 313pp. 6⅛ x 9¼.
21445-1 Paperbound $2.00

Prices subject to change without notice.

Available at your book dealer or write for free catalogue to Dept. Adsci, Dover Publications, Inc., 180 Varick St., N.Y., N.Y. 10014. Dover publishes more than 150 books each year on science, elementary and advanced mathematics, biology, music, art, literary history, social sciences and other areas.